GENESIS

TURN IT ON AGAIN

D1615345

THE ILLUSTRATED GENESIS STORY

Omnibus Press

London/New York/Sydney/Cologne

© Copyright 1983. This edition
© Copyright 1984 Omnibus Press
(A division of Book Sales Limited)
Book designed by Moira Kardi
Picture research by Valerie Boyd
Typeset by Capital Setters, London W1
Printed in England by The Thetford
Press Ltd, Thetford, Norfolk.

ISBN 0.7119.0442.1
UK Order No. OP 42761

Exclusive distributors:

Book Sales Limited
78 Newman Street. London W1P 3LA. UK

Omnibus Press
GPO Box 3304. Sydney. NSW 2001.
Australia

To the Music Trade Only:

Music Sales Limited
78 Newman Street. London W1P 3LA. UK

Special thanks to Tony Smith, Carol
Willis, Gail Colson, Brian Murray-Smith,
Alex Sim, Tony Stratton-Smith, Steve
Weltman, Lisa Bonnichon, Charisma
Records, Phonogram and Atlantic
Records, to Ricky Coppola and Ulrich Lill
for help with their collections, to Peter
Starie, Ed Hanel, to Judy and to the
many who have contributed details over
the years.To Genesis, thank you for the
music.
    For Genesis friends and fans across
the world.

CONTENTS

A SHORT HISTORY
PAGE 5

INTRODUCTION
PAGE 21

SINGLES-WORLDWIDE
PAGE 23

ALBUMS-WORLDWIDE
PAGE 37

SOLO EFFORTS
PAGE 50

COMPILATIONS
PAGE 92

COVERS
PAGE 97

PRODUCTION WORK
PAGE 100

BOOTLEGS
PAGE 103

TAPES
PAGE 111

BIBLIOGRAPHY
PAGE 117

PROGRAMMES
PAGE 119

VIDEO FILMS
PAGE 121

CONTACT
PAGE 125

The New Studio Album from
GENESIS

Featuring the single, "Mama."

Produced by Genesis with Hugh Padgham
Management: Tony Smith, Hit & Run Music

On Atlantic Records and Cassettes

Major tour November, 1983 through February, 1984

GENESIS
A SHORT HISTORY
BY STEVE CLARKE

FROM CHARTERHOUSE TO MEGA-STARS

None of the so-called 'progressive rock' bands that emerged in the early Seventies have proved so durable as Genesis. They amazed observers by surviving the apparently crippling departure of Peter Gabriel in 1975, and in commercial terms went from strength to strength in the years that followed, despite the palace revolution of punk which was designed to overthrow 'dinosaurs' like them.

In fact Genesis showed themselves to be considerably more adaptable than many who attempted to overthrow the old guard in the wake of 1976 and all that. Gabriel's departure gave the individual members of Genesis an opportunity to pursue solo careers that have produced some of the most interesting music of the late Seventies and early Eighties. It also created an environment for Phil Collins to develop as a musician within Genesis, which in turn gave him the confidence to develop his own successful solo career. The other members of Genesis have also been able to follow individual paths, while ensuring that Genesis remains a performing and recording entity.

Unlike, say The Who, or, musically nearer to home, Yes, Genesis has been able to have its cake and eat it. Whether this state of affairs can continue indefinitely remains to be seen. Other acts have not been able to manage it, but Genesis has always been something of an anomaly within the rock hierarchy.

Those who insist that it's impossible to deviate as far as Genesis have from traditional rock modes and still retain the music's essential qualities dismiss Genesis as 'pomp-rock'. The once fashionable appellation 'progressive-rock' has long been used strictly as a pejorative. The description evokes visions of conceited musicians playing purely for their own satisfaction, self-indulgent amidst vast banks of keyboards and dry ice. Genesis has never really belonged to this school of 'art-rock', the term preferred by Amercian critics.

Of course Genesis has always been strong on performance values – on putting on a show. But then so has David Bowie, not to mention The Rolling Stones or, come to that, The Sex Pistols and The Clash. Artifice has always been part and parcel of rock, as it has any other form of show business. That Genesis have always made a point of avoiding the street life stereotype of rock is to be admired, not disparaged. The fact that the group was formed at one of England's better known public schools only made matters worse with those who demand that every rock star should at least affect a working class style.

As the group's more recent success in the singles chart shows, Genesis are fundamentally a song band. Their one-time drummer Bill Bruford, hot from stints with Yes and King Crimson, was right when he said: "Genesis are actually a song group. And quite lightweight at that too. They don't even like to be considered very 'heavy' or anything like that."

Moreover, their enormous popularity came not as a result of extensive press lobbying but from genuine popular support. Genesis, for all their apparent complexity, are very much a people's band, and it is perhaps this consistent popularity that accounts for their longevity. Phil Collins is as much a people's hero as Rod Stewart. Significantly, Collins was not public school educated, unlike Peter Gabriel, Tony Banks and Mike Rutherford.

The English public school system has been held responsible for many of the things that make English society what it is. With its élitism, discipline and emphasis on team games, it is not the sort of institution generally regarded as an incubator for aspiring rock musicians. The relaxed atmosphere at provincial art schools has more often been a breeding ground for British rock musicians, while public schools have produced the upper ranks of the military and clergy, leading politicians and members of the professions. John Lennon, Pete Townshend, Eric Clapton and Joe Strummer are just four of the many British rockers to have experienced life as a student in an English art school. The number of bands formed in this environment during the last 25 years could fill a small volume. By contrast, only one British rock band of note has its beginnings in an English public school.

Peter Gabriel and Tony Banks entered Charterhouse School in the autumn of 1963, the year Britain started to buzz with The Beatles. Though not as prestigious as Eton or Harrow, Charterhouse has roots stretching back to the Carthusians, an order of monks founded in 11th century France, and those educated at Charterhouse are still known as Carthusians. The school was founded in 1611, orginially in London. The present school, situated in the prosperous Home Counties at Godalming, Surrey, dates from 1872.

These facts doubtlessly were rammed home to Gabriel and Banks, neither of whom found Charterhouse much to their liking in their early days at the school. Both were shy, sensitive boys who shared a hatred of the playing field but discovered a common interest in pop music, then undergoing its biggest upheaval since Elvis. Both were great Beatles fans, and it's likely that in the staid atmosphere of Charterhouse these hirsute Liverpudlians were even more attractive to two middle class boys from the Home Counties. Both had musical families on their mother's side, and they had each learnt to play piano as young children. Gabriel stopped taking lessons when he was nine and by the time Banks got to Charterhouse he too had grown bored with formal piano lessons. Later, under the direction of one of the Charterhouse masters. he re-discovered his enthusiasm for the instrument. At the same time as he was grappling with classical scores he also began to play by ear the pop songs he heard on the radio. Gradually he began to compose his own numbers, often incorporating more difficult chord progressions than commercial pop tunes.

As an adolescent Gabriel played drums and his fascination with rhythms would find an outlet in his post-Genesis career. At Charterhouse he and Banks listened to American soul music. Otis Redding and James Brown were great favourites. Already Gabriel's favourite instrument was the human voice. He would drum along to soul sounds or sing as Banks fingered the changes to a song from the Stax catalogue. They started writing songs together and formed a group, Garden Wall. The dreamy Gabriel, whose father was something of an electronics genius, took a shine to flower power, and at an end of term concert in the summer of 1966 showered the Charterhouse audience with rose petals.

Garden Wall were opening the show for The Anon, another Charterhouse group that featured Anthony Phillips on lead guitar and Mike Rutherford on rhythm. Rutherford had gone up to Charterhouse a year later than Banks and Gabriel but his prowess as a guitarist (he had played since he was eight) won him a role in The Anon. It was from the disintegration of these two fledgling groups that Genesis formed their first line-up in the winter of 1967, prompted by an old boy, Jonathan King, who in the two years since leaving Charterhouse had caused a minor sensation by writing and recording a Top Five record, despite his still being at university.

Jonathan King was just 21 when he had his first hit – a whimsical song, "Everyone's Gone To The Moon". That was in 1965. He followed it up by writing and producing "It's Good News Week" for Hedgehoppers Anonymous, a tongue-in-cheek protest song that confirmed his command of bubblegum styles. By the time the embryonic Genesis contacted him with their tapes he was working as assistant to the head of Decca Records, Sir Edward Lewis.

Anthony Phillips, Tony Banks, Peter Gabriel and drummer Chris Stewart recorded half a dozen songs at a friend's house. Initially Phillips sang – after all, five of the six numbers were written by him in collaboration with Rutherford – but once the rest of the band heard Gabriel's vocals on the Gabriel-Banks composition, "She's Beautiful", it was decided that Gabriel should sing all the numbers. King liked some of the song ideas and the quality of Gabriel's voice, and offered the band a contract, which they signed for a one year term.

King's finely tuned commercial sensibility encouraged his fellow Carthusians to stick to basics in their song writing, which tended to be elaborate. A second tape was rejected by King because it was too complex. Gabriel and Banks responded by writing a Bee Gee pastiche, "The Silent Sun", knowing that King would respond to its blatant commerciality. Their assumption was correct, and "The Silent Sun" was duly released on Decca in February 1968. The name Genesis was King's idea, and the following March the full fruits of the Genesis/King collaboration were released. "From Genesis To Revelation" was very much King's baby. Phillips for one was "disgusted" with the way the group had been manipulated by the shrewd popster who, in his opinion, had over-produced the album.

"From Genesis To Revelation" and the early singles (a second single, "A Winter's Tale", was released in 1968) failed to register with the public. These were heady days for pop and the record buying audience had plenty to choose from. Established acts like The Beatles and The Stones were still in full creative thrust. Everywhere new 'progressive' bands were rearing their shaggy heads. Pop was taking itself a lot more seriously as musical values appeared to replace commercial priorities.

For the individuals who comprised Genesis it was time to make some hard decisions about the future. Banks had gone up to Sussex University. Gabriel was considering a place he'd been offered at the London School of Film Technique. Phillips and Rutherford were both keen to concentrate their energies on the band and try to earn a living from Genesis. The relationship with King and Decca had petered out and once again Genesis were offering their music in the market place. That summer they recorded another demo, including versions of "White Mountain" and "Dusk" but these songs were turned down by a publisher, a decision which influenced Genesis' determination to finally turn professional.

That autumn and winter Genesis spent much of their time rehearsing at a remote country cottage. In September 1969 they played their first gig. By the turn of the year they were performing on the club and college circuit. Genesis would open their sets with a series of acoustic numbers before building up the pace with their more dramatic material. Gabriel has recalled: "We talked at length about set structuring. We would start with soft numbers and work up to the aggressive ones. If we kept the power in the back, we could introduce ouselves slowly like a folk band, and people would think, 'OK, just another acoustic band'. You could ignore us or not. And then we would gradually introduce more and more electric instruments and then we would finish off with "The Knife", this aggressive number about this revolutionary figure on a power trip. I knew that we had the power and the balls to grab the audience, and that if we hadn't got them by then, we would move them, one way or the other. They could not ignore that."

And they didn't. Their power as a performance band began to attract audiences, and by early 1970 the music business started to show fresh interest. Two newly formed labels were particularly fascinated by Genesis – the Moody Blues' Threshold Records, and Island Records. The latter had established itself as a record company prepared to stick its neck out and back new, pioneering talent. Island's acts included Traffic, Free, Spooky Tooth, Fairport Convention and King Crimson whose debut album, "In The Court Of The Crimson King", exerted a great influence on Genesis during this period.

As the Encyclopedia of Rock (Panther) remarks: "King Crimson were the prototype British 'progressive' band of the late Sixties." The band's guiding light was Robert Fripp whose guitar and, particularly, mellotron (then a new instrument) dominated Crimson's baroque arrangements. The lyrics of Pete Sinfield were similarly extravagant – surreal and fantastic. Crimson paved the way for many of the early Seventies' successful acts, especially Yes and Emerson, Lake & Palmer; Greg Lake was Crimson's original singer. But, unlike Yes and ELP, Fripp was bright enough never to allow his band to get the better of him. Crimson's impact on Genesis would soon be apparent, and Fripp would later work closely with Gabriel in his solo career.

Genesis' success on the club circuit was such that they were offered a residency upstairs at Ronnie Scott's world famous Soho jazz club in the spring of 1970. It was here that they were spotted by the A & R scout of a newly formed record company, Charisma Records. John Anthony was so impressed with Genesis that the next week he brought his boss to see them. Tony Stratton-Smith, a former sports journalist with a passion for the turf, formed Charisma in the late Sixties to nurture home grown talent but the label had yet to make the impact of Island or Chrysalis by breaking a band in its own right. In 1970 its most successful act was The Nice but another of its bands, Lindisfarne, was showing great promise.

As time would tell, Genesis were well suited to this quirky label who appeared not to rush things with their acts. Stratton-Smith has said: "They were rather like a young classic racehorse – if you work them too hard too early, they'll just burn out." The Charisma boss clearly saw Genesis as a long term investment. "I saw them as a band that was still putting together its own language, an album band, and therefore a concert band, a band to whom you had to make a two or three year commitment, whatever it cost. It was a long extended gamble but luckily by that time the whole shift of interest had gone over to the album artist, and away from the slick pop artist who could churn out hit singles. The market was right for Genesis in that sense."

Genesis' first album for Charisma, "Trespass" (October 1970) was not, however, a commercial success. Anthony had tried hard to capture the potency of the live band but Genesis clearly still had some way to go to find themselves in the studio. King Crimson were an obvious influence on the Genesis of "Trespass" – the staccato snare drumming recalled Mike Giles' distinctive playing on "In The Court Of The Crimson King". The mellotron was familiar too, but overall Genesis weren't as tight as Fripp's band and too often their lyricism became ponderous. Gabriel, however, came across as a distinctive singer with a range of expression not often found in rock.

Recording "Trespass" was not easy and after its completion Anthony Phillips stunned his colleagues by announcing he was leaving. The intense perfection of Genesis had become too much for the guitarist. His guitar work was an integral part of the Genesis sound and he played a major part in writing the material. Phillips' decision to quit at such a crucial time created a mood of uncertainty, and Banks for one considered following Phillips' lead. Instead, Genesis decided to rethink their position. The first move was to replace John Mayhew, Genesis'

drummer for the past year. Finding a new guitarist was a more difficult task.

Since their days at Charterhouse Genesis had experienced problems with drummers. They'd played now with three different drummers in as many years, none of whom had firmly established themselves. This time they wanted to make sure they made the right choice. An ad was placed in the Melody Maker: "Tony Stratton-Smith requires drummer sensitive to acoustic music, and acoustic 12 string guitarist."

Phil Collins was one of 15 drummers who auditioned. His playing was just what they needed and Collins' warm, ebullient personality was a welcome contrast to the stiff upper lips of Gabriel, Banks and Rutherford. Collins had been a child actor and played the Artful Dodger in the West End production of Oliver. He dreamed of being a football star but drumming was an early obsession. He came from Chiswick in West London and went to the local grammar school. Collins had played in several bands and was currently drumming with an undistinguished outfit called Flaming Youth.

Genesis had still not found a permanent replacement for Phillips when at the end of 1970 Gabriel replied to an ad in Melody Maker from a guitarist looking for work: "Guitarist/writer seeks receptive musicians determined to strive beyond existing/stagnant musical forms." The guitarist, Steve Hackett, lived up to his words. After four years together Genesis finally found the line-up that would establish them as an international attraction.

It would take Genesis another two years or so before they became a major rock act in Britain. They took another small step up the ladder when they stole the show at the opening night of the first Charisma package tour, at London's Lyceum in early 1971. Genesis were the opening act on a bill that also featured Lindisfarne and headliner Van Der Graaf Generator. Each of these acts had still to establish themselves but it was Genesis, the least known of the three, who made the strongest impression at the important London gig.

That summer they recorded their second album, "Nursery Cryme", released in the autumn of 1971. In Britain the record did little to advance Genesis' career but elsewhere in Europe it charted, much to the relief of all concerned, including Tony Stratton-Smith who was disappointed with the album. At the time Charisma was putting all its weight behind Geordie band Lindisfarne, their current top record sellers. In Italy "Nursery Cryme" was a top five album.

As the Italian success of ELP, King Crimson and even Van Der Graaf Generator showed, the Italians had a taste for rock music that was more in keeping with their own cultural traditions. Said Mike Rutherford: "Italy saved us because they reacted to that album. England gave us a really hard time on it."

Actually "Nursery Cryme" was a major step forward for the band. The new boys, Hackett and particularly Collins, gave Genesis an authority not apparent before on record. The guitarist has said that it took him some months to find his feet in the band but Hackett's performance on '"Nursery Cryme" belies any lack of ease he experienced during his first months with Genesis. Like Phillips before, Hackett's deft 12-string playing was essential to the group's sound. Moreover, his solos had an originality that suited his colleagues' pioneering spirit.

On "Nursery Cryme" Phil Collins plays with the kind of confidence not normally associated with a musician still barely in his 20s. Genesis needed a drummer who could ring the changes, often within the same song and Collins' intuitive skills filled this demanding role with great panache. As time would tell, the precocious drummer had that rare ability to combine technical expertise with what musicians describe as 'feel'. Collins' technique encompassed everything from pop to jazz. He was Ringo Starr, Phil Seaman and John Bonham rolled into one.

As songwriters Genesis had come a long way. Their imagination brought a unique English eccentricity to pop and bizarre tales like "Harold The Barrel" and "The Musical Box" became established stage favourites. Gabriel would introduce these songs with off-the-wall narratives that gave a Genesis concert another dimension and frequently had the audience in stitches.

As 1971 gave way to 1972 Genesis' reputation as an extraordinary live band gained ground rapidly. By this time they had begun to include "Supper's Ready" and "Watcher Of The Skies" in their increasingly theatrical sets, two songs that would make the upcoming "Foxtrot" album such a milestone in their career.

In the early Seventies a reaction had set in to the studied scruffiness of the fashionable bands of the late Sixties, when it was obligatory for groups to turn up on stage wearing the clothes they'd apparently got up in. The Faces had a sharpness that hadn't been seen at a pop concert since the Mod days of the mid-Sixties. Marc Bolan went one step further by applying make-up, and Alice Cooper and David Bowie made a point of turning a rock concert into a show.

The term 'glam-rock' was coined to describe this latest pop fashion.

Genesis could hardly be called 'glam-rock' but Gabiel's increasing use of costume and the band's efforts to stage a show meant they were part of the general move back towards performance rock. Great pains were taken to disguise their stage equipment. Elaborate lighting became part of a Genesis gig, and later lasers would be deployed. Genesis' literary songs, with their Alice In Wonderland collection of characters, were ideal for this theatrical treatment. In early 1973, by which time "Foxtrot" had charted, Genesis played London's Rainbow Theatre, then the most prestigious gig in Britain. It was a seminal concert for Genesis, with Gabriel appearing in a series of bizarre outfits to illustrate the group's songs.

The material on "Foxtrot", released in autumn 1972, was even more adventurous than the songs of its predecessor, "Trespass". Yet despite the complexity of "Supper's Ready", a fascinating juxtaposition of ideas that retained their cogency against all odds, the song was accessible in a way that past Genesis material had never been. Years earlier Banks and Gabriel had learnt the deceptively simple skills of crafting a pop song and these elements still informed their songs, no matter how elaborately they were arranged. "Watcher Of The Skies", for instance, was based on a very simple riff.

"Foxtrot" gave Genesis their first number one – in Italy. In March 1973 they undertook their first ever headline tour of Britain. A live album, released that summer, enlarged their audience still further. It was unusual to release a live LP at this stage in a band's career and Genesis were reluctant to do so. But "Genesis Live" offered those who'd been impressed by the band in performance a snapshot of Genesis in concert. The record sold well. From now on it would be relatively easy for Genesis to retain their European success.

Inevitably America was a different story. The band played their first American gigs in late 1972 when they were surprised by the warm welcome from a New York audience. Genesis' music was such that they couldn't introduce themselves to the country by playing as support to star bands; it was impossible to compress their set into 45 minutes. New York might have been a success of sorts, but throughout the rest of the United States Genesis had nothing beyond a cult following. It would be a long haul before the group made a nationwide impact on the world's major rock market.

In the autumn of 1973 Genesis released their second album of the year, "Selling England By The Pound". One track, "I Know What I Like (In My Wardrobe)", graced with an immediately recognisable refrain, duly gave Genesis their first British hit single. The album was a major success commercially. If no two songs had the immediate impact of "Watcher Of The Skies" and "Supper's Ready", overall it was a more satisfying record. The inclusion of Collins' doleful vocal on the song he co-wrote, "More Fool Me", added a new facet to Genesis and allowed him to step out from behind the drums for the first time and perform a number live. The song was poles away from the histrionics of "The Battle Of Epping Forest", aurally an ungainly number, but justified by Gabriel's lyrics, which depict a show-down between two rival East End gangs, puns and all. Elsewhere fact and fantasy combined to make "Selling England By The Pound" an invigorating set.

The same year Genesis renewed their contract with Charisma albeit on terms more favourable to them. The group's business organisation still left something to be desired, however. Apart from the obliging hand of Tony Stratton-Smith and the odd accountant and lawyer, Genesis had never had a manager as such. In the past they had approached concert promoter Tony Smith but he turned them down. They now went to Smith again and this time he accepted the commission. Smith's father John, also an impresario, had promoted an early Beatles tour. His son became a mechanical engineer but he'd been bitten by the show-biz bug and for some years now had co-promoted shows with his father. He was astonished to find out how much Genesis were in debt and claims that it was not until 1976 that the band went into the black.

1974 appeared to augur well for Genesis. The previous December they'd played six successful concerts at The Roxy Club on Los Angeles' Sunset Strip. In the New Year Genesis received rave reviews for their five nights at London's Drury Lane theatre, an unusually smart setting for a rock band. An NME Readers' poll voted Genesis Top Stage Band, ahead of ELP, The Who, Pink Floyd and Yes. But Peter Gabriel was beginning to have his doubts about his future with the band.

Perhaps the trouble started when film director William Friedkin invited Gabriel to write a script for him; Friedkin had recently created a stir with his supernatural movie, The Exorcist. Naturally Gabriel was flattered by the approach. His work with Genesis as a

writer and performer suggested that he could operate in other areas and his keen visual sense indicated that film might be an appropriate medium. It seems that Tony Banks, Gabriel's close friend at Charterhouse, delivered an ultimatum to Gabriel – choose either Genesis or the movie script but not both. The outcome of this uncomfortable situation was that Genesis' music no longer benefitted from a mutual exchange of ideas between all concerned; the ensuing "The Lamb Lies Down On Broadway" LP produced a broad division of labour where Banks, Rutherford, Hackett and Collins provided the music *to* Gabriel's words. At the same time Gabriel was willing to give up some of the limelight to his colleagues; witness the appearance of Phil Collins as a featured vocalist in recent months.

In retrospect Gabriel has agreed that he might have bitten off more than he could chew by insisting that he write all the album himself. "I had very arrogantly stuck my neck out and said, 'I've got to write the whole thing', and then I couldn't do it in the time. In the end, Tony and Mike gave me a hand and wrote the lyrics on 'The Lamb Lies Down On Broadway' on Side Four," he said later.

Concept albums have had a chequered history in rock. Only The Beatles' "Sgt. Pepper" has received wholehearted approval and even then it's questionable whether "Sgt. Pepper" is really a concept album and not a disparate collection of songs united by one song, "Sgt. Pepper's Lonely Hearts Club Band." There is no attempt by Lennon and McCartney to tell a story as such. Certainly The Who's "Tommy" has received its fair share of criticism and their "Quadrophenia" has also been surrounded by controversy. "The Lamb" is no exception. Ten years after its release people still argue over its merits. Its main fault is that too many ideas are crammed onto its four sides. It does not, however, deserve to be classed with Yes's absurdly conceited "Tales From Topographic Oceans", the album that led to Rick Wakeman's departure from the group.

Unlike Yes and "Topographic Oceans", Gabriel's motives in writing "The Lamb" are not to be doubted. Like Townshend on "Tommy" and "Quadrophenia", he was genuinely attempting to broaden the group's horizons. Moreover, Gabriel had the ability to stand back from the project and apparently understand why some failed to respond to "The Lamb". As he said in March 1975: "It's quite a barrage of words and there should be an award for people who go through it." Significantly, none of Gabriel's subsequent music has attempted so grand a scale. In fact the music that he made after the two year silence that followed his leaving Genesis was in many ways more straightforward than anything Gabriel had ever recorded with Genesis. After "The Lamb" Genesis gradually streamlined their music too and, as far as they were concerned, concept albums were a thing of the past.

At the time any qualms they had about "The Lamb" weren't apparent. In November 1974 they began a mammoth 102 date tour that would introduce audiences in North America and Europe to this latest offering from a band that was about to undergo its first serious personnel crisis since Anthony Phillips walked out after "Trespass" in 1970.

Genesis had never believed in compromise and rather than gradually introduce audiences to "The Lamb" track by track, the tour was based around the album in its entirety. Gabriel's songs in the past had combined elements of fact, fantasy and legend but never before had Genesis audiences had to face demands such as "The Lamb Lies Down On Broadway" presented. On stage Gabriel played the part of the album's central figure, Puerto Rican New Yorker Rael, caught up in a surreal adventure, the complexity of which belied the simple leather jacket and jeans Gabriel wore for the part. Even so Gabriel detected a surprising change in the audience that came to see Genesis. "The leather jacket and jeans I wear as Rael has given us a more raunchy appearance, and we can sense a change in the audience", he said. The tour opened in America, where the group had just signed with Atlantic Records, a collaboration that would be more profitable than Genesis' relationship with their previous American distributor, Buddah.

Genesis had barely got into the rhythm of touring when in December Gabriel told his colleagues that he was leaving. Despite efforts to persuade him to rethink his decision, Gabriel held firm. In November 1975 he explained why he had left to a disbelieving public: "The vehicle we had built as a co-op to service our songwriting became our master and had cooped us up inside the success we had wanted. It affected the attitudes and the spirit of the whole band. The music had not dried up and I still respect the other musicians, but our roles had set in hard. To get an idea through to Genesis the Big meant shifting a lot more concrete than before. For any band, transferring the heart from idealistic enthusiasm to professionalism is a difficult operation. I believe that the use of sound and visual images can be

developed to do much more than we have done . . . As an artist, I need to absorb a wide variety of experiences . . . I had begun to think in business terms . . . but treating records and audiences as money was taking me away from them."

Later Gabriel was less diplomatic about what was happening to Genesis during his last days with the group. He told a journalist in 1977: " The success we had so badly wanted when we were beginning was, in the end, a trap. Once we'd achieved that massive popularity we couldn't develop with any freedom. There were so many people involved, and so much money involved in the band that it seemed a risk to try to change. Everything was geared to preserve us as we were. I wanted and needed to change.

"There were all sorts of games that went on. Very silly, unnecessary games. And because I used to get all the publicity, there was resentment and jealousy, which didn't make things any easier.

"We weren't exactly friendly when I announced I was leaving.

"One of the things I felt about Genesis, in fact, was that we promised more than we actually delivered . . . I think we were better ideas men than we were realisers. Looking back, I can see that there was a lot we should have done – and done more succinctly . . . The way the band actually approached its material was at fault . . . too often the band was too concerned with contrived chord sequences and changes and patterns. The melody and the lyric – which I was often concerned with – were secondary. Much of the time the arrangements were too busy."

Gabriel's first solo single, "Solsbury Hill", recounted his feelings about how he felt trapped by the group he had done so much to create. But that was almost two years away. At the time the question mark in most people's minds was what would happen to Genesis.

Some were under the incorrect impression that Genesis was Gabriel and that without him they would surely become defunct. The "Lamb" tour revolved around him as a front-man more than any other Genesis tour. Lyrically, give or take a few lines, the album was his creation. In the past it was Gabriel who was most sought after by the press, primarily because of his visual impact on stage. Because of this it was assumed that Gabriel wrote the bulk of Genesis' songs.

Those predicting the imminent demise of Genesis were encouraged in their belief when that year both Steve Hackett and Phil Collins became involved with projects outside the band. Hackett recorded his first solo album, "Voyage Of The Acolyte", released in the autumn of 1975. Weeks later Collins played his first gig with Brand X at the London School of Economics. Featuring the remarkable Percy Jones on bass, Robert Lumley on keyboards and guitarist John Goodsall, Brand X was a free-blowing jazz-rock ensemble that allowed the restless drummer the opportunity to draw directly on his love for the highly acclaimed Weather Report, the band formed by disgruntled jazzers Wayne Shorter and Josef Zawinul in 1970. In fact Collins' involvement with the surprisingly excellent Brand X posed no threat to Genesis and probably served as a tonic to the musician during this period of upheaval.

Meanwhile Genesis began work on the backing tracks of their next album, "A Trick Of The Tail", for release in early 1976. As the recording progressed it became increasingly clear that finding Gabriel's successor was no easy task. Hundreds of tapes arrived from would-be Genesis singers and at one point the group considered introducing a black singer. But the answer to their problem was much closer than they realised. During the recording of the album's heaviest number, "Squonk", Collins suggested that he should sing. The result impressed Banks, Rutherford and Hackett, who from past experience knew that Collins could handle vocals on their more melodic songs. Peter Gabriel's 'replacement' had been within their ranks all along without anyone realising it.

Producer David Hentschel has suggested why it took so long for them to hand over the vocals to Collins: "Probably nobody really thought of using him because he had such a significant musical part in the band".

Collins' similarity to Gabriel as a singer was quite uncanny. Observed Tony Stratton-Smith: "He sounded more like Peter Gabriel than Peter Gabriel." The ensuing album and subsequent tour, complete with Bill Bruford on drums, silenced the doubters who thought that without Gabriel Genesis were a non-starter. "A Trick Of The Tail" won unanimous approval and in the States sold better than all Genesis' previous albums.

A casual listener would be hard-pressed to tell the difference between this post-Gabriel recording and those that the departed singer had made with the band. A more careful appraisal revealed music that lacked Gabriel's surreal touch. Genesis' characteristic whimsicality was still there and the band still told stories but somehow the music

was less unpredictable, safer than before. "A Trick Of The Tail" was easier to listen to than "The Lamb" and "Selling England By The Pound". Overall Genesis had tightened up. Significantly, "A Trick Of The Tail" won over listeners who had previously found Genesis heavy going.

On stage too Genesis became more accessible. Collins' tuition at the Barbara Speake Stage School came into its own as the drummer-turned-singer demonstrated his ability to project a song on stage. Phil Collins had effected a remarkable transition. The 'new' group chose America to break itself in during the spring of 1976. Their enhanced power as a *playing* band (Collins and Bruford played in tandem for parts of the show) was particularly noticeable on new material like "Squonk" and the instrumental "Los Endos."

Later Gabriel spoke about how his departure gave Genesis new life: "At the time of my leaving they said I'd destroyed things for them and was being selfish. It was only gradually that they got back their own self confidence . . . I think my leaving in fact kicked some fresh air into the band . . . I felt if I hadn't left Genesis it would have become obsolete or rather it would have become obsolete if we'd gone on as we were."

Mike Rutherford's assessment of the situation was similar to Gabriel's. He said: "To have a change like that at such an advanced stage in the band's career really brought home to me, and I think to everyone else, the fact that we really had to work hard . . . Suddenly there wasn't that sense of security there had been. That doesn't mean we weren't confident, but however confident you are there are still fears; the ground was taken away from under us a bit and that really motivated us to work hard. As a result "Trick Of The Tail" was more of a challenge that it would otherwise have been, and meeting it really pulled us together as a group.

"I think we all changed a bit in that situation. Funnily enough, in a way it made us all more relaxed and calm with each other. It could just be number, I think four is easier than five, and three is probably easier than four. It gives people more room to breathe."

By the end of the year another Genesis album was in the can. "Wind And Wuthering" was released in the New Year. As Rutherford told Sounds, it was a less immediate album than its predecessor. "On "Wind And Wuthering" there are certain things which catch your attention on the first listen but the album as a whole only begins to emerge after a few more plays. It's a very gradual album in that sense, although it actually took us less time to record than any other album in the past and our working procedure was exactly the same". The record broke no new ground for Genesis but was a solid, reliable set that sustained the group's by now superstar status.

Genesis promoted the album by playing a British tour, including dates at the refurbished Rainbow Theatre. It was here that fans were introduced to Chester Thompson, Genesis' new drummer who replaced Bruford, now immersed in session work. To play with a musician who'd gigged recently with Weather Report was something of a personal triumph for Phil Collins. "I wanted to make sure we had someone with impeccable taste and class," he enthused.

Thompson's pedigree was indeed beyond reproach. In addition to keeping time with Weather Report, Thompson's past included a stint with the equally fastidious Frank Zappa. The drummer hailed from Baltimore. He was surprised at how demanding Genesis were to work with. "Genesis is the most different thing I have ever had to adapt to, the most difficult because it was the most different. When I joined Genesis I went in with the attitude that their stuff would be really easy and simple, but when I got to really sitting down there and playing with the cats, it was different", he said. That Genesis' music could accommodate the drumming of a black American who'd played with Weather Report signified how Genesis had developed from their early days as an English progressive rock band. Genesis weren't about to surrender to the finger-poppin' rhythms of jazz-funk but as a live band there was no doubting how much *feel* the group could now muster.

That spring and summer Genesis' hectic touring schedule included headlining at New York's Madison Square Garden and a trio of stadium gigs in Brazil, for which a jumbo jet was chartered to transport the group and their 28 tons of hardware. In June they played three gigs at London's massive Earls Court exhibition hall. These dates were to be Steve Hackett's last with the band.

In a press release Hackett highlighted the problem: "With so many composers in the group, it was difficult to ensure everybody got a fair slice of the writing cake. The band's selection process was rather arbitrary. Although I was satisfied with my contribution to the last Genesis album, "Wind And Wuthering", I actually had enough material of my own to fill an entire album."

Genesis were surprised by the guitarist's decision to quit. They thought that the problems that initially arose over how many songs Hackett should contribute to "Wind And Wuthering" had been resolved by the guitarist's intention to make another solo album *and* remain in Genesis. Collins told NME that October: "Steve could have done everything he's doing now – and stayed in Genesis".

According to the drummer, Hackett demanded that a quarter of "Wind And Wuthering" should be given over to his songs. "We just don't do things like that," explained Collins. "We use the best material that's around. Steve's attitude was unreasonable – but at the same time, understandable".

Ironically, Hackett's departure affected the sound of Genesis much more than Gabriel's leaving had. The subsequent album, "And Then There Were Three" (who said Genesis didn't have a sense of humour?), confident though it was, sounds very different from its two predecessors. Inevitably Banks' keyboards dominate the album. The result is a much more monochromatic sound than the 'old' Genesis; Hackett's tranquil 12-string and deceptively potent solos had given the band a lot of colour. Now that he was gone, Genesis' response was to rely less on the music and more on the songs. As a result "And Then There Were Three" consisted of *eleven* songs, a lot for Genesis. These were necessarily less elaborate than much of Genesis' previous material. An edited version of the closing number, "Follow You Follow Me", proved the point by giving the group their first British Top Ten hit. Despite the coming of the New Wave, the album was a huge success.

Hackett's on-stage replacement was Daryl Stuermer, a 25 year-old American recommended by Alphonso Johnson, late of Weather Report and a friend of Collins. Johnson himself was invited to join the band but when things didn't work out, he suggested Stuermer who already knew Chester Thompson. Stuermer's past was as much jazz as rock; he had worked with Jean-Luc Ponty and George Duke.

Stuermer's introduction to live work with Genesis was very much a baptism of fire. Their 1978 touring schedule was likely to put hair on anyone's chest. Within eight months they played around 100 gigs in three continents, including their first shows in Japan. This marathon included three separate visits to the States. For recording purposes Genesis might be down to a trio but on the road it was a different matter, with an entourage of royal proportions. Their touring equipment included six enormous hexagonal, computerised mirrors, programmed to revolve and rotate with the music. As Tony Smith told the press: "With a band like Genesis who don't have a Jagger or a Mercury or a Rotten you need to make the show visually as well as aurally entertaining."

It was a gruelling year for the band, made all the worse by the scenes taking place off stage. This intense touring put undue strain on Collins' marriage and later he complained that Genesis had become "slaves to the road". He moaned: "We'd meet people at the end of the tour who had been working for us and we didn't even know their names. After that we decided to turn it all back". In other words, the theatrics and the scale of presenting the show had got on top of Genesis. 1979 would be a year to put Genesis on ice.

GABRIEL
GOING IT ALONE

By the late Seventies Genesis had, as they admitted, become too big for their own good. It was a situation that Peter Gabriel had seen coming when he left the band in 1974. Indeed, according to Gabriel, Genesis were already trapped by the "machinery" of the rock business when he decided to pull out.

Since quitting Genesis Gabriel has consistently avoided such a state of affairs affecting his own output. Gabriel's typically idiosyncratic solo career (each of his four studio albums has the same title – Peter Gabriel) has been characterised by a desire not to compromise, to make music on his own terms. As a performer he refused resolutely to be sucked into the helter-skelter of stadium-rock, something which he just avoided with Genesis.

Cynics might suggest that as a solo act Gabriel does not have that kind of ability. If that is the case, then they are unfamiliar with his albums or his concerts. There is no doubt that had Gabriel concentrated his energies on selling out the biggest venues there are, he would have succeeded.

His music might not always have been what his record company was looking for, but to date he has made enough 'commercial' tracks to silence the doubters.

Gabriel did not leave Genesis so that he could become a star for the second time around. He left because he wanted to control his music and the way he made it. In this he has succeeded admirably.

When Gabriel re-united with Genesis for a one-off gig in 1982 he did so with considerable reluctance, and was quite candid in admitting that the concert was only taking place to raise funds lost by the commercial failure of the World of Music, Arts and Dance Festival (WOMAD), in which he was a prime mover.

Immediately after playing his last gig with Genesis in May 1975 Gabriel went to earth. True to his word he spent a lot of his time with his family at his home near Bath. Perhaps sensing that a major upheaval was about to happen in British rock, Gabriel took stock of his situation. It was not until early 1977 that he re-emerged with a new album and tour. By then all hell had broken loose. "Hippie bands", like Genesis, were being castigated for their old and decadent ways. Inspired by the abrasive anarchy of The Sex Pistols, the punks argued that rock should be given back to the kids. Rock was a people's music and you didn't need tons of expensive hardware or, come to that, musical skills, to play it. The music should be played in intimate clubs and it should be "relevant" to the lives led by its audience. "Kids were bored with listening to their elder brother's Pink Floyd albums and smoking his old joints", said one proponent of punk. The new wave was upon us.

Public school-educated Gabriel did not lack sympathy with many of these attitudes. Later Gabriel would work with various new wave performers, including members of The Jam and XTC. After all he had left Genesis because they had become too big. Which is not to say that Gabriel was part of the New Wave. Nonetheless his first solo album reflected the directness of the new music. Gone were the elaborate time changes of Genesis and gone too were the flamboyant costumes.

The 'new' Peter Gabriel retained his eccentricity but visually and musically he was generally in step with the times. Much of the music on "Peter Gabriel" (1) came straight from the heart. Gabriel hadn't stopped trying to be clever but there was less of it. He summed it up when he said of his recorded début: "I think it is simpler, more direct emotionally, more personal than much of what I've done previously, and I think it takes itself less seriously." The exquisite "Solsbury Hill", a big hit in Britain, was a case in point. Clearly autobiographical (Solsbury Hill is a place near Gabriel's home), this euphoric paean to self determination made direct reference to how he felt during his latter days with Genesis. Gabriel's humour was apparent on "Excuse Me", replete with barbershop quartet vocal. The erstwhile Genesis singer's gift for writing a strong melody came through on "Humdrum" and "Here Comes The Flood", neither of which would have been out of place on a Genesis record, albeit with more elaborate arrangements.

The album was recorded in Canada with American producer Bob Ezrin and mainly American musicians. Gabriel has said that of all the producers he has worked with, none had the control that Ezrin exerted on this first LP. Herein lies the record's chief fault. For in retrospect "Peter Gabriel" (1) lacks the single-mindedness of future Gabriel albums. By choosing a producer with a reputation for working with such notorious acts as Lou Reed and Alice Cooper, perhaps Gabriel was being deliberately perverse. Whatever, the record established Gabriel as a songwriter in his own right.

Meanwhile the singer made his live début in New York, where the audience was less familiar with Gabriel (and less prejudiced) than the British fans. By the time he played London in the summer of 1977 he had gained sufficient confidence to convince observers that Peter Gabriel was every bit as fascinating an act as Genesis. Naturally Gabriel was still concerned with surprising and even shocking audiences, but his on-stage persona was untheatrical in the sense that props, save for a radio mike, were now dispensed with. Gabriel also surprised audiences by including in his set versions of Tamla Motown classics. It seems that every re-birth entails renewing contact with the roots and Peter Gabriel was no exception.

One of the musicians who played on Gabriel's début was guitarist Robert Fripp. Since the late Sixties Fripp had piloted various King Crimson line-ups but recently had been working with another of British rock's more esoteric musicians, Brian Eno, an early refugee from Roxy Music. Gabriel's respect for Fripp dated back to the earliest days of King Crimson. Fripp sat in with Gabriel on stage and ended up producing Gabriel's second album.

Tony Levin (bass) and Larry Fast (synthesizer), now long standing members of Gabriel's live band, were retained from the first album. One 'newcomer' was keyboard player, Roy Bittan, from Bruce Springsteen's E Street Band. Gabriel's apparent preference for working with American musicians wasn't just a matter of taste. He said: "The fact that I'm an ex-public school boy and come from the school of progressive rock would have put a lot of musicians off working with me (in Britain). At least they'd have to like me *despite* those things."

Fripp's production was more sympathetic to Gabriel than Ezrin's had been, but despite the record's authority, "Peter Gabriel" (2) failed to build on the success of its predecessor. That rousing song of disaffection, the great "D.I.Y.", did not follow "Solsbury Hill" up the charts when it was released as a single. For my money, "Peter Gabriel" (2) is an embarrassment of riches even if it is more traditional than the records that followed it. Several of the numbers spotlighted Gabriel's skills as a social observer – "Mother Of Violence", "A Wonderful Day In A One-Way World", "Animal Magic" and "D.I.Y." These trenchant songs reflected a sensibility that echoed the disenchanted voices of the New Wave but "Peter Gabriel" (2) failed to win over much in the way of new support for the former Genesis star.

Such was Gabriel's commercial standing in America at the time that, after hearing his third album, Atlantic Records refused to release it. Commercial pressures were something that Gabriel had no intention of succumbing to and when the record finally came out, it did so on Mercury. The irony of the situation was not lost on Gabriel when a song from the album, "Games Without Frontiers" became one of the surprise hits of 1980 on both sides of the Atlantic.

After the commercial disappointment of "Peter Gabriel" (2) the singer was back in public favour with a song culled from an album that was avowedly experimental. Not that Gabriel went out of his way to make a hit single. "Singles are primarily advertising for the album. If I get a hit, I'm delighted, but it has nothing to do with what I'm trying to do," he said later.

"Games Without Frontiers" was Gabriel at his quirky best, highly original and unpredictable. As this song shows, Gabriel's zest for the whimsical was now tempered by an incisiveness not always apparent with Genesis. Another song from the album, "Biko", also created a stir and was released as a single after DJs began playing it. The number was a sort of elegy to the black South African activist Steve Biko, murdered by the authorities whilst in captivity. It was the sort of song John Lennon might have written with its simple refrain and tribal chanting.

Gabriel wasn't interested only in the politics of Africa. He was also increasingly attracted to African rhythms and other exotic sounds not often heard in rock. Both this album and its successor were written with what Gabriel called "a rhythm-based . . . method". In part this derived from Gabriel making use of new technology, like the programmable drum box. He said: "I've been looking for more interesting rhythms than are found in most rock music. I've been listening to non-European music and old Tamla records, and inventing patterns, so I had 40 or 50 rhythms before I started writing. This meant I could write differently, often giving more space to the music than I would without having rhythm first."

Gabriel's interest in rhythm went back to his days at Charterhouse and before, when he played the drums. But Gabriel was not content with leaving rhythm just to a conventional drum set-up. For "Peter Gabriel" (3) drummers Jerry Marotta and Gabriel's old colleague Phil Collins dispensed completely with cymbals. It is surprising what a difference this made to the overall sound. "The drum kit . . . is not the only God-given rhythm source," Gabriel observed. "I still use drums because they are very exciting and very quick to get something active and fluid. I would like to work with a lot more different rhythmic bases."

Tracks like "Intruder", "No Self Control" and "Lead A Normal Life" exemplified Gabriel's new attitude to making music. Gabriel's first two albums confirmed his songwriting abilities. Now he was concerning himself with the *sound* of the songs. Lyrically, Gabriel's material was more direct than his earlier solo efforts, with less word play and alliteration. He admitted that lyrics weren't of an over-riding importance to him: "I spend about 40 per cent of my compositional time on lyrics. They're not throwaway items, but they aren't the primary interest". Not all of "Peter Gabriel" (3) looked ahead. Melodically, at least one song, "Snapshot", recalled early Seventies Genesis, although new approaches to old instruments and new instruments left no doubt that Gabriel was of the Eighties.

Two years elapsed between Gabriel's third and fourth albums, interspersed with the release of a live album, no doubt for contractual reasons. As Gabriel said: "It's very important for me not to get caught up in the tour-album-tour-album trap. Record companies would be much happier if artists produced albums every nine months, but I've been in this too long to feel so motivated by success that it should exclude all other things from my life."

One project Gabriel involved himself with was the World of Music, Arts and Dance Festival (WOMAD). He explained the project in the following terms: "We tried to harness this fashion that was developing with people like Bow Wow Wow, Adam and the Ants, the Brian Eno/ David Byrne/ Holger Czukay/Can type of experiments, all this stuff – to get an audience to move one stage further down the line and listen to the source material. About 20 or 30 per cent of what we heard really excited us; we figured that if we could get turned on by this, perhaps a lot of other people could as well.

"I originally had the idea (for WOMAD) on a much smaller scale, and I turned it over to the people at The Bristol Recorder (a fanzine). My role in the whole thing was peripheral. I was still making my album while they were working on it 24 hours a day, and I didn't want it to seem as if I was getting the publicity they deserved. I was useful in making phone calls to musicians, lawyers, record company and TV people. Also, that I was guaranteed to appear helped convince other artists it wasn't just a fly-by-night charity gig."

The festival "lost a packet" and to raise money Gabriel re-grouped with Genesis for a one-off concert in the autumn of 1982. Steve Hackett joined the group for an encore of "I Know What I Like (In My Wardrobe)", but the reunion was strictly for the sake of expedience and afterwards all parties resumed their separate careers.

In America Gabriel's fourth album was released on the relatively new Geffen Records, Gabriel's third label in four albums. Gabriel appeared pleased with his new distributor, the first he actually chose for himself: "Geffen has the attitude of giving artists room to develop, even if it means making mistakes. There aren't a lot of people in the business that take that attitude. They are looking for long-term artists, not hit-makers who might be dropped after one failure – as happened to me on that other label."

How the relationship develops remains to be seen. On one point it has already got the better of Gabriel insofar as the album was titled "Security" instead of plain Peter Gabriel. The singer agreed reluctantly to have "Security" adorn a label stuck on the shrink wrap but it turned up on the record label as well. Geffen claimed it was a mistake.

"Peter Gabriel" (4) was even more exotic in its influences than its predecessor. The second side, opening with the high-tech disco of "Shock The Monkey", is probably the best music Gabriel has recorded since his departure from Genesis. Drums and percussion dominate an aural landscape that has one foot in the past (a Ghanaian drum section on "Rhythm Of The Heat") and one in the future, as Gabriel experiments with the latest in instrumental technology. He explains: ". . . I tried to create a sound library, mainly working with a Fairlight CMI synthesizer, which has the facility of recording live sound. We went to scrapyards, factories, wind tunnels and university engineering departments as well as trying to get a whole range of conventional instruments as they normally sound, and as they normally *don't* sound – squeaks, taps, breath noises and all the rest."

But in the same breath that Gabriel embraces the latest technology, he writes 'about' cultures much older than our own, using instrumentation from those cultures, like the Ethiopian pipes at the beginning of "The Family And The Fishing Net". This contrast between two cultures is clear in the exquisite "San Jacinto", where Gabriel depicts the co-existence of primitive and Western cultures in an American resort. In this aspect Gabriel's music recalls some of Joni Mitchell's songs on "The Hissing Of Summer Lawns" and "Don Juan's Reckless Daughter". Gabriel's solo music often has an emotional impact not usually associated with Genesis. The penultimate "Wallflower" on "Peter Gabriel" (4) comes straight from the heart.

Solo careers are difficult to sustain in rock. Often the music is self-indulgent and bereft of ideas, as the ego obstructs an artiste's judgement. Throughout the course of four highly individual and typically idiosyncratic records, Gabriel has more than vindicated his decision to quit Genesis. Moreover, he has pursued his career on his own terms without the business or his audience misleading him into less creative pastures. Peter Gabriel looks well set for the rest of the Eighties. In his case, a little goes a long, long way.

GENESIS IN THE EIGHTIES (EPILOGUE)

When Genesis returned to work in 1980 they hadn't released an album in almost two years. In the interim each of the trio that remained inevitably turned his attention to individual projects. Banks and Rutherford released their first solo albums, "A Curious Feeling" and "Smallcreeps Day" respectively. It does neither an injustice to say that each record illustrates why the two musicians are best operating within Genesis. Collins continued working with Brand X. It would be another year before his own solo album was released.

Bank's and Rutherford's solo albums failed to make much commercial impact but there were other reasons for making them. As Collins said: "I know what people say about solo albums, but in our case, I can only say that doing them actually kept Tony and Mike in the band. The group is solid. Solo albums, if they're approached from the right context, don't mean the artist is bored with the band. They give him a chance to get some things out of his system and build up his confidence in himself as an individual."

As the 'come-back' album showed, Genesis was solid and even breaking new ground. "Duke" marked the emergence of Collins as a writer of real influence with the group. The effect was to make Genesis more direct and more emotional. The musical economy of "Turn It On Again", another Top Ten hit in Britain, made the point. Collins had sound melodic sense, and one of his down-beat songs, "Misunderstanding" was a major American hit. "Alone Again" was credited to Rutherford but it was delivered by Collins with maximum commitment.

In contrast to the 1978 mega-tour, this time around Genesis made a point of playing smaller venues, often where audiences rarely got the opportunity to see bands of their status. Genesis even returned to Aylesbury, scene of their earliest triumphs back in the days of "Nursery Cryme" and "Foxtrot".

As naive as it sounded, it was hard not to believe Collins when that year he told a reporter: "We started playing for music and that's how it continues . . . we think one of the secrets of our success is that we trundle on irrespective of fashion." Unlike the majority of bands, Genesis had never relied on fashion, except possibly for a brief time in the early Seventies. "You must remember that for most of the time we've been in existence, we've been thought unfashionable," observed Rutherford. Fashion might be all right at the time but as Genesis have proved, not being fashionable has its advantages.

In 1981 a critic reviewing one of Genesis' London shows pinpointed the influence Phil Collins was exerting within the band: "Their latest recordings bear unmistakeable traces of a desire to reduce their music to a more modest and manageable scale. Almost certainly this has been promoted by the success of the solo album released a year ago by Phil Collins, their singer, part-time drummer and co-composer, wherein he avoided the baroque excesses of pomp-rock in favour of stylist pop songs borrowing intelligently from the modes of the moment."

Collins' first solo album, "Face Value", had indeed shaken a lot of people's preconceptions. That the drummer's musical interests extended beyond the elaborately arranged confines of Genesis was long apparent vis-à-vis his continued work with Brand X. Gabriel's exit, moreover, had given Collins the opportunity to show off his skills as a singer and performer. These considerable achievements were, however, about to be put into a different perspective as Collins now proved his credentials as an extraordinarily gifted music maker in his own right.

Significantly, in feel and content, "Face Value" was a different set-up to Genesis, give or take the odd melody line. As if to illustrate the point, Collins included a re-arranged song, "Behind The Lines" from the last Genesis album, "Duke". In its new setting the song is barely recognisable as Collins gives it an unabashed funk treatment. For the album Collins had assembled an all star cast, including the horn section from Earth, Wind & Fire. It was this strident brass section from one of America's top black acts that set the pace on "Face Value". Collins showed himself to be a clever song-writer, with what seemed like an innate understanding of pop. The single from the album, "In The Air Tonight", might well have made the British Number One slot were it not for the sudden commercial interest in John Lennon, caused by that great musician's tragic death; it shouldn't be forgotten that "Face Value" contained a splendid pastiche of Lennon's chunk of off-the-wall Sixties' psychedelia, "Tomorrow Never Knows". In retrospect "In The Air Tonight" is archetypal Collins – dramatic, atmospheric and featuring some ferocious stickmanship from the man himself. The mixture would later be repeated for "Mama", a hit for Genesis in 1983. "Face Value" is a gem. The record also indicated Collins' skill as a producer. Later Collins would act in this role for such diverse talent as John Martyn and Anni-Frid from Abba.

The repercussions for Genesis following the success of "Face Value" have already been suggested. Their next album,

"Abacab", produced by Hugh Padgham (who engineered "Face Value") was their most incisive to date. Genesis' eleventh studio album ranks as their finest set since "A Trick Of The Tail", albeit for very different reasons. The title track is a no-holds-barred tour de force on which Collins and Banks positively shine. The unashamed clever pop of "No Reply At All", replete with horns courtesy of Earth, Wind & Fire, was a clear by-product of Collins' solo work. Five years ago, who would have thought Genesis would record with Earth, Wind & Fire? Collins told the press: "Because I've had different things to do every time I come back to the group, it's different. I've learnt something from some other projects I've done and I bring that into the group."

Genesis entered their second decade with a bang, and it was now common practice for them to make regular successful assaults on the singles charts, in addition to sustaining their position as an albums band. The following year, 1982, witnessed another two solo albums from the Genesis fold, Rutherford's "Acting Very Strange" and Collins' "Hello, I Must Be Going". The former was a brave attempt by the bassist to sing his own material but it was overshadowed by Collins' album. Here the formula was similar to before and again the drummer brought the benefit of Eighties studio technology to bear on a golden great from the Sixties. The result, a brilliant re-creation of the Tamla Motown classic, "You Can't Hurry Love", gave Collins his first number one single in January 1983.

The flurry of solo activity put back the release of a new Genesis studio album to autumn of 1983. In the meantime "Three Sides Live" had to suffice. The undoubted highlight of this set, recorded at Genesis concerts in Europe and America, was a blast from the past, the closing "It"/"Watcher Of The Skies", culled from 1976 when Bill Bruford and Steve Hackett were with the band.

At the time of writing Genesis' most recent album, "Genesis", looks like being the band's first album to produce a hat trick of hit singles. Already the afore-mentioned "Mama", and "That's All" have proved their commercial worth. The jokey "Illegal Alien" looks like following the same path.

As an album "Genesis" carries on where "Abacab" left off, though Banks' keyboards are less dominating and there is nothing of the same degree of potency as in "Abacab" itself. Collins' intuitive pop sensibility shows no sign of losing its influence on the band but the album lacks the depth of "Abacab".

Collins is contracted to produce one

more album for Virgin. Banks is reported
to be working on his album. There is also
talk of other projects, including film
scores. Whatever, the band is adamant
that they shall continue to work as an
entity, provided that it continues to be
fun.

If only Jonathan King had known
what he was about to start all those years
ago at Charterhouse.

A SHORT HISTORY

GENESIS

IN CONCERT

A FILM OF LAST SUMMER'S UNFORGETTABLE TOUR

FEATURING THE UNIQUE MUSIC CONCEPT OF

Rick Wakeman

ROYAL WORLD CHARITY PREMIERE in the presence of
H.R.H. THE PRINCESS ANNE Mrs Mark Phillips
and Captain Mark Phillips
in aid of B.A.F.T.A. on Monday, 31st January, 1977 at 8.30p.m.

WHITE ROCK

★ STARTS TUES. 1st FEB ★
Shaftesbury Avenue
Licensed Bar

ABC 1
Tel: 836 8861

ALL SEATS BOOKABLE AT THEATRE BOX-OFFICE
NO POSTAL APPLICATIONS

Every effort has been made to ensure that this discography is as complete as possible, for which I thank Genesis friends and fans throughout the world. Omissions, however, are inevitable – especially when dealing with the more remote markets. Genesis singles and albums have been listed in separate sections with their international variations. Owing to the difficulty in ascertaining the exact day of release, which frequently differs from published information, listings for the most part include only month and year.

The Genesis Singles section covers Genesis single and EP releases around the world, all of which are 7″ unless otherwise noted. Country codes used are UK for United Kingdom, US for United States, EUR for Europe, JAP for Japan, GER for Germany, HOL for Holland. FRANCE, ITALY and SPAIN are detailed in full. Choice of single releases has increasingly tended to differ for each territory. In Europe, there are various incidences where the catalogue number has remained the same and the picture sleeves have differed for each country, and vice versa. 'The Carpet Crawlers' is variously listed on record as 'Carpet Crawl' and 'Carpet Crawlers' – the official reason for this is not known. All the earlier releases now constitute valuable collector's items. Musicians on each single release can be found by checking against the album listing for the same period.

The Genesis Albums section covers all official studio and live releases. The extensive listing of Decca re-issues, all taken from 'From Genesis To Revelation' and the first three singles, have been included at their dates of release for the sake of context. 'Genesis Live' was actually deleted in the UK at one point as Genesis were reportedly not happy with the sound quality, but was soon returned to the catalogue through pressure from

imports. Where special labels have been used, especially on later releases, these have been included.

Unofficial record and tape releases are included for the sake of completeness. The author and publishers stress that these are strictly illegal releases, and have no knowledge as to how these can be obtained. All errors in song titles, etc., are the fault of the bootleggers. Song credits can be taken as for the official releases.

The solo sections cover albums and singles listed together, plus other appearances and contributions, from Genesis members past and present. Chester Thompson and Daryl Stuermer join Genesis for live work, and are featured on the new live album.

Any additions or amendments will be much appreciated, and can be sent to P.O. Box 107, London N6 5RU, England.

Thank you all for putting a little *Charisma* into a dozen categories

1. THE SILENT SUN (Genesis)/
THAT'S ME (Genesis)
UK Decca F1 2735.
Released 22nd February 1968.
Mono – different matrix number to the
album version which is stereo.

SINGLES

2. THE SILENT SUN (Genesis)/
THAT'S ME (Genesis)
US Parrot 45-PAR 3018.
USA. promo only, not released.
Parrot Records distributed by London
Records Inc.

3. A WINTER'S TALE (Genesis)/
ONE EYED HOUND (Genesis)
UK Decca F12775.
Released 10th May 1969.

5. IN THE BEGINNING (Genesis)/ THE SERPENT (Genesis)
ITALY Decca F22909 (picture sleeve).
Released 1969.

6. LOOKING FOR SOMEONE (Genesis)/VISIONS OF ANGELS (Genesis)
UK Charisma GS 1.
Promo copy 1970, not released.

4. WHERE THE SOUR TURNS TO SWEET (Genesis)/IN HIDING (Genesis)
UK Decca F12949.
Released 27th June 1969.
Taken from 'From Genesis To Revelation'.
Photograph is of demonstration copy.

SINGLES

7. THE KNIFE Part I (Genesis)/ THE KNIFE Part II (Genesis)
UK Charisma CB152 (picture sleeve).
Released 1971.
Track is 'The Knife' from 'Trespass' split into two halves.

8. HAPPY THE MAN (Genesis)/ SEVEN STONES (Genesis)
UK Charisma CB181 (picture sleeve).
ITALY Philips 6073 316 (picture sleeve).
Released October 1972.

9. WATCHER OF THE SKIES (Genesis)/WILLOW FARM (Genesis)
UK No release.
US Charisma CAR 103.
EUR Charisma 6073 331 (picture sleeve).
Released 1973.
A-Side different mix to album version.

10. TWILIGHT ALEHOUSE (Genesis)
UK Charisma – one-sided flexidisc. No catalogue number.
Produced by Genesis.
Issued free with Zig Zag Magazine October 1973, and to first 1,000+ UK Genesis Information members October 1976.

11. I KNOW WHAT I LIKE (Genesis)/TWILIGHT ALEHOUSE (Genesis)
UK Charisma CB224.
US Charisma FC-26002.
FRANCE Charisma 6073 347 (picture sleeve).
ITALY Charisma 6073 347 (different picture sleeve).

Released February 1974.
Genesis' first UK single success 6th April 1974.
Weeks in chart: 7.
Highest UK chart placing: 21.

12. COUNTING OUT TIME (Genesis)/ RIDING THE SCREE (Genesis)
UK Charisma CB238.
EUR Charisma 6073 357 (picture sleeve).
ITALY Charisma 6073 357 (different picture sleeve).
Released November 1974.
Illustration is German sleeve.

13. THE LAMB LIES DOWN ON BROADWAY (Genesis)/ COUNTING OUT TIME (Genesis)
US ATCO 7-013.
Released 1974.

14. THE CARPET CRAWLERS (Genesis)/EVIL JAM (THE WAITING ROOM live) (Genesis)
UK Charisma CB251.
Released April 1975.
B-side recorded live at Los Angeles Forum.

15. CARPET CRAWL (Genesis)/ THE LAMB LIES DOWN ON BROADWAY (Genesis)
ITALY Charisma 6073 363 (picture sleeve).
Released 1975.

16. A TRICK OF THE TAIL (Banks)/ RIPPLES (Rutherford/Banks)
UK Charisma CB277.
Released March 1976.

17. RIPPLES (Rutherford/Banks)/ IT'S YOURSELF (Banks/Collins/ Rutherford/Hackett)
ITALY Charisma 6073 378 (picture sleeve).
Released 1976.

18. ENTANGLED (Hackett/Banks)/ A TRICK OF THE TAIL (Banks)
FRANCE Charisma 6073 381 (picture sleeve).
Released 1976.

**19. RIPPLES (Rutherford/Banks)/
ENTANGLED (Hackett/Banks)**
US ATCO 7-050.
Released 1976.

**20. YOUR OWN SPECIAL WAY
(Rutherford)/IT'S YOURSELF
(Banks/Collins/Rutherford/Hackett)**
UK Charisma CB300.
EUR Charisma 6073 393 (picture sleeve).
Released February 1977.
Highest UK chart placing: 45.
Illustration is German sleeve.

**21. YOUR OWN SPECIAL WAY
(Rutherford)/....IN THAT QUIET
EARTH (Hackett/Rutherford/
Banks/Collins)**
US ATCO 7-076.
Released 1977.
Also mono/stereo promo 45-7076.

**22. SPOT THE PIGEON EP: MATCH
OF THE DAY (Banks/Collins/
Rutherford)/PIGEONS (Banks/
Collins/Rutherford)/INSIDE AND
OUT (Banks/Collins/Rutherford/
Hackett)**

UK Charisma GEN 001 (picture sleeve
7").
EUR Charisma 6228 204 (white border
picture sleeve 7").
AUSTRALIA Charisma 6200 032 (green
& white sleeve 12", black vinyl).
CANADA Atlantic EP 1800 (B&W picture
sleeve 12", limited edition blue vinyl).
CANADA Atlantic EP 1800 (B&W picture
sleeve 12", black vinyl).
Released May 1977.
Recorded at same time as 'Wind and
Wuthering'.
Highest UK chart placing: 14.

**23. FOLLOW YOU FOLLOW ME
(Banks/Collins/Rutherford)/
BALLAD OF BIG (Banks/Collins
/Rutherford)**
UK Charisma CB309 (picture sleeve).
EUR Charisma 6079 461 (picture sleeve).
Released March 1978.
Highest UK chart placing: 7.

SINGLES

**24. FOLLOW YOU FOLLOW ME
(Banks/Collins/Rutherford)/
BALLAD OF BIG (Banks/Collins/
Rutherford)**
JAP Charisma SFL-2257 (picture sleeve
plus A-side lyrics).
Released 1978.

**25. FOLLOW YOU FOLLOW ME
(Banks/Collins/Rutherford)/
INSIDE AND OUT (Banks/Collins/
Rutherford/Hackett)**
US Atlantic Records.
Released 1978.
A-side is a different mix.

**26. MANY TOO MANY (Banks)/ THE
DAY THE LIGHT WENT OUT
(Banks)/VANCOUVER (Collins/
Rutherford)**
UK Charisma CB315 (picture sleeve).
GER Charisma 6228 205 (picture sleeve
includes tour dates).
ITALY Charisma 6079 467 (picture
sleeve).
JAP Charisma SFL-2322 (picture sleeve
plus A-side lyrics).
Released June 1978.
Highest UK chart placing: 43.

**27. GO WEST YOUNG MAN (DEEP
IN THE MOTHERLODE) (Rutherford)/
SCENES FROM A NIGHT'S DREAM
(Collins/Banks)**
US Atlantic 45-3511.
JAP Charisma SFL-2342 (picture sleeve
with A-side lyrics, album discography).
Released 1978.
US release also issued in 12″ version.

**28. TURN IT ON AGAIN (Banks/
Collins/Rutherford)/BEHIND THE
LINES PART II (Banks/Collins/
Rutherford)**
UK Charisma CB356.
EUR Charisma 6173 523 (picture sleeve).
JAP Charisma SFL-2478 (picture sleeve
plus A-side lyric).
SPAIN Charisma 6079 493 (picture sleeve,
title in Spanish)
Released March 1980.
Highest UK chart placing: 8.

**29. MISUNDERSTANDING (Collins)/
BEHIND THE LINES (Banks/Collins/
Rutherford)**
US Atlantic 45-3662 (picture sleeve).
Released 1980.

**30. DUCHESS (Banks/Collins/
Rutherford)/OPEN DOOR
(Rutherford)**
UK Charisma CB363 (picture sleeve).
Released May 1980.
Highest UK chart placing: 46.
B-side non album track.

**31. MISUNDERSTANDING (Collins)/
DUCHESS (Banks/Collins/
Rutherford)**
GER Charisma 6000 462 (picture sleeve).
Released 1980.

**32. TURN IT ON AGAIN (Banks/
Collins/Rutherford)/EVIDENCE OF
AUTUMN (Banks)**
US Atlantic 45-3751.
Released 1980.
B-side non album track.

**33. TURN IT ON AGAIN (3.27)
(Banks/Collins/Rutherford)/TURN
IT ON AGAIN (4.47) (Banks/Collins/
Rutherford)**
US Atlantic PR 369 (promo sleeve).
Released 1980.
US only – 12″ promo.
B-side is live recording from London
Lyceum 1980.

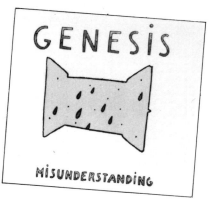

**35. ABACAB (Banks/Collins/
Rutherford)/ANOTHER RECORD
(Rutherford/Banks/Collins)**
UK Charisma CB388 (picture sleeve,
initial copies with picture label).
GER Vertigo 6000 711 (picture sleeve).
SPAIN Vertigo 7PP-46 (6000 711) (picture
sleeve plus lyrics).
JAP Vertigo 7PP-46 (6000 711) (picture
sleeve plus lyrics)
Released August 1981.
Highest UK chart placing: 9.

**36. NO REPLY AT ALL (Banks/
Collins/Rutherford)/DODO (Banks/
Collins/Rutherford)**
US Atlantic 45-3858.
Released 1981.
Also double A-side promo – short version
(4.00)/standard version (4.37).

**34. MISUNDERSTANDING (Collins/
EVIDENCE OF AUTUMN (Banks)**
UK Charisma CB369 (picture sleeve).
Released August 1980.
B-side non-album track.
Highest UK chart placing: 42.

**37. KEEP IT DARK (Banks/Collins/
Rutherford)/NAMINANU (Banks/
Collins/Rutherford)**
UK Charisma CB391 (picture sleeve 7″).
Released October 1981.
B-side is a non-album track.
Highest UK chart placing: 33.

38. KEEP IT DARK (Banks/Collins/
Rutherford)/NAMINANU (Banks/
Collins/Rutherford)/ABACAB (Long
Version) (Banks/Collins/Rutherford)
UK Charisma CB391-12 (picture sleeve
12").
Released October 1981.
'Naminanu' is a non-album track,
'Abacab' is the album version.

39. NO REPLY AT ALL (Banks/
Collins/Rutherford)/NAMINANU
(Banks/Collins/Rutherford)
HOL Vertigo 6000 748 (picture sleeve 7").
HOL Vertigo 6400 534 (picture sleeve
12").
Released 1981.
B-side is a non-album track.

40. ABACAB (Banks/Collins/
Rutherford)/WHO DUNNIT? (Banks/
Collins/Rutherford)
US Atlantic 45-3891.
Released December 1981.

41. MAN ON THE CORNER (Collins)/ SUBMARINE (Banks/Collins/ Rutherford).

UK Charisma CB393 (picture sleeve).
US Atlantic 45-4025 (different picture sleeve).
EUR Vertigo 6000 786 (different picture sleeve).
Released March 1982.
B-side is non-album track.
Highest UK chart placing: 41.

SINGLES

I KNOW WHAT I LIKE (IN YOUR WARDROBE)
(Genesis)
GENESIS
Producer: John Burns/Genesis

CB.224

42. 3 x 3 EP: PAPERLATE (Banks/Collins/Rutherford)/YOU MIGHT RECALL (Banks/Collins/ Rutherford)/ME AND VIRGIL (Banks/Collins/Rutherford)

UK Charisma GEN 1 (picture sleeve).
UK Charisma GEN 1 (picture disc).
Released May 1982.
Tracks not released on album in the UK.
Highest UK chart placing: 8.

43. PAPERLATE (Banks/Collins/ Rutherford)/YOU MIGHT RECALL (Banks/Collins/Rutherford)
US Atlantic 45-4053 (picture sleeve)
EUR Vertigo 6000 831 (picture sleeve)
JAP WEA P-1686 (picture sleeve)
Released June 1982.

44. THE LADY LIES (LIVE) (Banks)
One-sided flexidisc on green vinyl free
with Flexipop Magazine.
UK Flexipop 021/LYN 11806.
Released August 1982.

45. 'GENESIS SOLO' FLEXIDISC
Free with 'Pop' Magazine, W. Germany.
GER LYN 7132.
Released 1979.
   Side One: Tony Banks 'For A While',
Brand X 'Don't Make Waves'.
   Side Two: Interviews with Tony Banks
and Phil Collins.

46. I KNOW WHAT I LIKE (IN YOUR WARDROBE) (Genesis)/COUNTING OUT TIME (Genesis)
UK Old Gold Records OG-9263.
Released January 1983.
Re-release of two original A-sides.

47. FOLLOW YOU FOLLOW ME (Banks/Collins/Rutherford)/ A TRICK OF THE TAIL (Banks)
UK Old Gold Records OG-9264.
Released January 1983.
Re-release of two original A-sides.

48. FIRTH OF FIFTH (LIVE) (Banks/ Rutherford/Collins/Gabriel/Hackett)
UK Genesis Information GI-01
Live flexidisc recorded in Nassau, Long
Island, N.Y. 1981.
Produced by Genesis. Limited edition
numbered sleeve.
Issued with Genesis Magazine from
Genesis Information.
Released May 1983.

49. MAMA (Banks/Collins/Rutherford)/IT'S GONNA GET BETTER (Banks/Collins/Rutherford)
UK Charisma/Virgin MAMA 1 (picture sleeve).
US Atlantic 7-89770 (picture sleeve).
EUR Vertigo 814 219-7.
Released August 1983.
Highest UK chart placing: 4.

50. MAMA (Long Version) (Banks/Collins/Rutherford)/IT'S GONNA GET BETTER (Long Version) (Banks/Collins/Rutherford)
UK Charisma/Virgin MAMA 1-12 (picture sleeve).
US Atlantic 0-86982 (picture sleeve).
Released August 1983.

UK Charisma/Virgin TATA 1 (picture sleeve).
UK Charisma/Virgin TATA Y-1 (picture disc – special shape).
Released November 1983.
Highest UK chart placing: 16.

52. THAT'S ALL (Banks/Collins/Rutherford)/TAKING IT ALL TOO HARD (Banks/Collins/Rutherford)/FIRTH OF FIFTH (LIVE) (Banks/Collins/Rutherford/Gabriel/Hackett)
UK Charisma/Virgin TATA 1-12 (picture sleeve).
Released November 1983.
'Firth Of Fifth' recorded live at The Savoy, N.Y. 1981.

53. THAT'S ALL (Banks/Collins/Rutherford)/SECOND HOME BY THE SEA (Banks/Collins/Rutherford)
US Atlantic 7-89724.
Released November 1983.

54. ILLEGAL ALIEN (Banks/Collins/Rutherford)/TURN IT ON AGAIN (LIVE) (Banks/Collins/Rutherford)
UK Charisma/Virgin AL 1 (picture sleeve).
UK Charisma/Virgin ALS 1 (special shape picture disc).
US Atlantic.
Released January 1984.

51. THAT'S ALL (Banks/Collins/Rutherford)/TAKING IT ALL TOO HARD (Banks/Collins/Rutherford)

55. ILLEGAL ALIEN (Banks/Collins/Rutherford)/TURN IT ON AGAIN (Extended Live Version) (Banks/Collins/Rutherford)

UK Charisma/Virgin AL 1-12 (picture
sleeve).
Released January 1984.

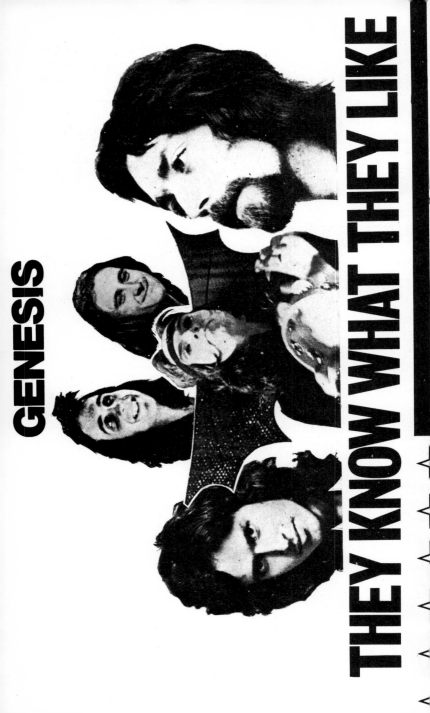

GENESIS

THEY KNOW WHAT THEY LIKE

ALBUMS

1. FROM GENESIS TO REVELATION
UK Decca SKL 4990.
US London PS643.
EUR Decca SKL 4990.
Released March 1969.
All titles composed and performed by
Genesis.
Produced by Jonathan King.
Recorded at Regent Studio B, London,
Summer 1968.
   Side One: 1. Where The Sour Turns To
Sweet/2. In The Beginning/3. Fireside
Song/4. The Serpent/5. Am I Very
Wrong?/6. In The Wilderness.
   Side Two: 7. The Conqueror/
8. In Hiding/9. One Day/10. Window/
11. In Limbo/12. Silent Sun/13. A Place To
Call My Own.
   Tony Banks keyboards, vocals. Peter
Gabriel lead vocal, flute. Anthony Phillips
guitars, vocals. Mike Rutherford bass,
guitars, vocals. John Silver drums.
David Thomas back-up vocals. Arthur
Greenslade string arrangements.
   Re-released in 1974 as 'Genesis – In
The Beginning' on same catalogue
number and with identical record, but
different sleeve.

2. TRESPASS
UK Charisma CAS 1020.
US ABC Records ABCX 816.
GER Charisma/Philips 6369 905.
JAP Charisma RJ7301.
Released October 1970.
All titles composed, arranged and
performed by Genesis.
Produced by John Anthony.
Recorded at Trident Studios, London,
July 1970.

Engineered by Robin Cable.
Tape Operator David Hentschel.
Sleeve artwork by Paul Whitehead.
  Side One: 1. Looking For Someone/
2. White Mountain/3. Visions Of Angels.
  Side Two: 4. Stagnation/5. Dusk/
6. The Knife.
  Tony Banks organ, piano, mellotron,
guitar, vocals. Peter Gabriel lead vocal,
flute, accordion, tambourine, bass drum.
John Mayhew drums, percussion, vocals.
Anthony Phillips lead guitar; acoustic
12-string, dulcimer, vocals. Mike
Rutherford bass guitar, acoustic
12-string, cello, vocals.

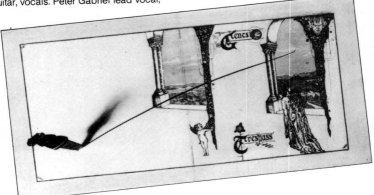

3. NURSERY CRYME

UK Charisma CAS 1052.
US Charisma CAS 1052 (Distributed by
Buddah Records.
GER Charisma 6369 916.
JAP Charisma RJ7302.
Released November 1971.
All titles composed, arranged and
performed by Genesis.
Produced by John Anthony.
Recorded at Trident Studios, London,
August 1971.
Engineered by David Hentschel.
Sleeve artwork by Paul Whitehead.
  Side One: 1. The Musical Box/
2. *For Absent Friends/3. The Return Of
The Giant Hogweed.
  Side Two: 4. Seven Stones/5. Harold
The Barrel/6. Harlequin/7. The Fountain
Of Salmacis.
  Tony Banks organ, mellotron, piano,
electric piano, 12-string, vocals. Phil
Collins drums, vocals, percussion. Peter
Gabriel lead vocal, flute, bass drum,
tambourine. Steve Hackett lead guitar,
12-string. Mike Rutherford bass guitar,
bass pedals, 12-string, vocals.
*Phil Collins lead vocals.
US release was in single sleeve only.

4. FOXTROT

UK Charisma CAS 1058.
US Charisma CAS 1058 (Distributed by Buddah Records).
GER Charisma 6369 922.
JAP Charisma RJ7303.
Released October 1972.
All titles composed, arranged and performed by Genesis.
Produced by David Hitchcock/Genesis.
Recorded at Island Studios, London, August-September 1972.
Engineered by John Burns.
Sleeve artwork by Paul Whitehead.
Sound – Richard Macphail.
Photographs by Armando Gallo, M. Nunn, G. Terrill, Barry Wentzell.
   Side One: 1. Watcher Of The Skies/ 2. Time Table/3. Get 'Em Out By Friday/ 4. Can-Utility And The Coastliners.

   Side Two: 5 Horizons/6. Supper's Ready: i) Lover's Leap, ii) The Guaranteed Eternal Sanctuary Man, iii) Ikhnaton And Itsacon And Their Band Of Merry Men, iv) How Dare I Be So Beautiful?, v) Willow Farm, vi) Apocalypse In 9/8 (co-starring the Delicious Talents of Gabble Ratchet), vii) As Sure As Eggs Is Eggs (Aching Men's Feet).
   Tony Banks organ, mellotron, piano, electric piano, 12-string, vocals. Phil Collins drums, vocals, percussion. Peter Gabriel lead vocal, flute, bass drum, tambourine, oboe. Steve Hackett lead guitar, 12-string and 6-string. Mike Rutherford bass guitar, bass pedals, 12-string, vocals, cello.
*Steve Hackett acoustic solo.
US release was in single sleeve only.

5. PRESENTING GENESIS

CANADA only – Charisma CAS 101.
Released 1973. Compilation of tracks taken from first three Charisma albums.
   Side One: 1. The Musical Box/ 2. Fountain Of Salmacis/3. Timetable.
   Side Two: 4. The Return Of The Giant Hogweed/5. The Knife/6. Seven Stones.

6. GENESIS LIVE

UK Charisma CLASS 1.
US Charisma CAS 1666.
GER Charisma 6499 593.
JAP Charisma RJ7225.
Released August 1973.
All titles composed, arranged and performed by Genesis.
Co-produced by John Burns/Genesis.
Recorded live by the US King Biscuit Hour Show at De Montford Hall, Leicester and Free Trade Hall, Manchester February 1973.
Tapes mixed at Island Studios, London.
Photography by Armando Gallo, Bob Gruen, Barry Wentzell.
   Side One: 1. Watcher Of The Skies/ 2. Get 'Em Out By Friday/3. The Return Of The Giant Hogweed.

   Side Two: 4. The Musical Box/ 5. The Knife.
   Tony Banks organ, mellotron, electric piano, 12-string, vocals. Phil Collins drums, vocals, percussion. Peter Gabriel lead vocals, flute, bass drum, tambourine. Steve Hackett lead guitar, 12-string. Mike Rutherford bass guitar, bass pedals, 12-string, 6-string.

7. SELLING ENGLAND BY THE POUND
UK Charisma CAS 1074.
US Charisma FC 6060 (Distributed by Atlantic Records).
EUR Charisma 6369 944.
JAP Charisma RJ7304.
Released September 1973.
All titles composed, arranged and performed by Genesis.
Produced by John Burns/Genesis.
Recorded at Island Studios, London August 1973.
Engineered by Rhett Davies.
Cover painting by Betty Swanwick, A.R.A.
  Side One: 1. Dancing With The Moonlit Knight/2. I Know What I Like (In Your Wardrobe)/3. Firth Of Fifth/4. More Fool Me.
  Side Two: 5. The Battle Of Epping Forest/6. After The Ordeal/7. The Cinema Show/8. Aisle Of Plenty.
  Tony Banks keyboards, 12-string. Phil Collins drums, percussion, vocals, lead vocals on 'More Fool Me'. Peter Gabriel lead vocals, flute, oboe, percussion. Steve Hackett lead guitar, nylon guitar. Mike Rutherford bass guitar, 12-string, electric sitar.
  Released in single sleeve with lyric sheet insert, except in Italy which featured a gatefold sleeve, photo on back cover, and Armando Gallo's Italian translation of the lyrics.

8. THE LAMB LIES DOWN ON BROADWAY (Double album)
UK Charisma CGS 101.
US ATCO SD 2-401.
EUR Charisma 6641 226.
JAP Charisma SFX 10022-3.
Released November 1974.
All titles composed, arranged and performed by Genesis.
Produced by John Burns/Genesis.

Recorded at Glosspant, Wales, with the Island Mobile Studio, and mixed at Island Studios, London, August/September/October 1974.
Engineered by David Hutchins.
Sleeve design and photography by Hipgnosis.
Sleeve notes by Peter Gabriel.
  Side One: 1. The Lamb Lies Down On Broadway/2. Fly On A Windshield/3. Broadway Melody of 1974/4. Cuckoo Cocoon/5. In The Cage/6. The Grand Parade Of Lifeless Packaging.
  Side Two: 7. Back In NYC./8. Hairless Heart/9. Counting Out Time/10. The Carpet Crawlers/11. The Chamber Of 32 Doors.
  Side Three: 12. Lilywhite Lilith/13. The Waiting Room/14. Anyway/15. Here Comes The Supernatural Anaesthetist/16. The Lamia/17. Silent Sorrow In Empty Boats.
  Side Four: 18. The Colony Of Slippermen: i) The Arrival, ii) A Visit To The Doktor, iii) Raven/19. Ravine/20. The Light Dies Down On Broadway/21. Riding The Scree/22. In The Rapids/23. IT.
  Tony Banks keyboards. Phil Collins drums, vocals, percussion, vibes. Peter Gabriel lead vocals, flute, and story. Steve Hackett lead guitar, guitars. Mike Rutherford bass guitar, 12-string.
  Eno responsible for 'Enossification' on 'The Waiting Room'. Choral contribution by Graham Bell.

9. GENESIS COLLECTION VOLUME ONE
UK only – Charisma CGS 102.
Boxed set including 'Trespass' and 'Nursery Cryme' in original sleeves plus poster.

10. GENESIS COLLECTION VOLUME TWO
UK only – Charisma CGS 103.
Boxed set including 'Foxtrot' and 'Selling England By The Pound' in their original sleeves plus poster.

Special price limited edition released April 1975. As the records were in their original sleeves, various unscrupulous record dealers simply threw away the boxes and sold the individual records at the full price – thus making these sets even more of a limited edition than originally planned!

11. REFLECTION ROCK THEATRE
GER only – Fontana 9299 515.
Released 1975.
　　Side One: 1. I Know What I Like/
2. Harold The Barrel/3. Harlequin/
4. Watcher Of The Skies/5. The Fountain of Salmacis.
　　Side Two: 6. Supper's Ready.
　　'Watcher Of The Skies' is a different recording.

12. A TRICK OF THE TAIL
UK Charisma CDS 4001.
US ATCO SD 36-129.
EUR Charisma 6369 974.
JAP Charisma RJ 7305.
Released February 1976.
All titles arranged and performed by Genesis.
Produced by David Hentschel/Genesis.
Engineered by David Hentschel and Nick Bradford.
Recorded at Trident Studios, London, November 1975.
Sleeve design by Hipgnosis, artwork by Colin Elgie.
　　Side One: 1. Dance On A Volcano (Rutherford/Banks/Hackett/Collins)/
2. Entangled (Hackett/Banks)/3. Squonk (Rutherford/Banks)/4. Mad Man Moon (Banks).
　　Side Two: 5. Robbery, Assault and Battery (Banks/Collins)/6. Ripples (Rutherford/Banks)/7. A Trick Of The Tail (Banks)/8. Los Endos (Collins/Hackett/Rutherford/Banks).
　　Tony Banks pianos, synthesizers, organ, mellotron, 12-string, backing vocals. Phil Collins lead vocals, drums, percussion. Steve Hackett lead guitar, 12-string. Mike Rutherford bass guitar, 12-string, bass pedals.
　　The original idea of 'All Titles Done By All' equal credits worked against the band as some people started assuming that the songs were mostly Peter Gabriel's work. From this first album following Gabriel's departure individual credits were noted for each song.

13. GENESIS IN CONCERT – LOS MELHORES MOMENTOS DA TEMPORADA NO BRASIL
Brazil only – Som Livre 404.7086.
Promotional compilation for Brazilian tour 1976.

ALBUMS

Side One: 1. Fountain Of Salmacis/
2. Can Utility And The Coastliners/
3. Dancing With The Moonlit Knight.
Side Two: 4. Ripples/5. I Know What I
Like/6. Stagnation.

Despite the title, this is not a live
album. All tracks taken from studio
albums.

ALBUMS

14. GENESIS R-O-C-K ROOTS
UK Decca ROOTS 1.
Released May 1976.
Same as 'From Genesis To Revelation'
but re-issued to include the early Decca
mono singles tracks 'The Silent Sun'/
'That's Me' and 'A Winter's Tale'/
'One-Eyed Hound'.

15. THE BEST .... GENESIS
US only – Buddah Records BDS-5659-2.
Released 1976.
Double album re-release combining
'Nursery Cryme' and 'Foxtrot'.

16. WIND AND WUTHERING
UK Charisma CDS 4005.
US ATCO SD 36-144.
EUR Charisma 9124 003.
JAP Charisma RJ7201.
Released January 1977.
All titles arranged and performed by
Genesis.
Produced by David Hentschel/Genesis.
Recorded at Relight Studios,
Hilvarenbeek, Holland, September 1976.
Remixed at Trident Studios, London,
October 1976.
Engineered by David Hentschel.
Assistant engineers Pierre Geoffroy
Chateau (Holland) and Nick Bradford
(London).
Sleeve design by Hipgnosis, artwork by
Colin Elgie.
Side One: 1. Eleventh Earl Of Mar
(Banks/Hackett/Rutherford)/2. One For
The Vine (Banks)/3. Your Own Special
Way (Rutherford)/4. Wot Gorilla? (Collins/
Banks).

Side Two: 5. All In A Mouse's Night (Banks)/6. Blood On The Rooftops (Hackett/Collins)/7. Unquiet Slumbers For The Sleepers . . . (Hackett/ Rutherford)/8. . . . In That Quiet Earth (Hackett/Rutherford/Banks/Collins)/ 9. Afterglow (Banks).

Tony Banks Steinway grand piano, ARP 2600 and Pro-Soloist synthesizers, Hammond organ, mellotron, Roland string synthesizer, Fender Rhodes piano, etc. Phil Collins lead vocals, drums, cymbals, percussion. Steve Hackett lead guitar, nylon classical guitar, 12-string, kalimba, auto-harp. Mike Rutherford bass guitar, 4-, 6-, 8-string, electric guitar, 12-string, acoustic guitar, bass pedals.

17. IN THE BEGINNING
US London Records Collector Series LC 50006.
Released 1977.
USA – only re-release of 'From Genesis To Revelation'.

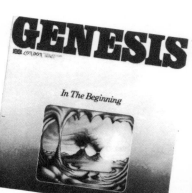

18. FROM GENESIS TO REVELATION
GER Nova Records (Decca) 6.21580.
Released 1977.
German – only re-release of 'From Genesis To Revelation'.

19. GENESIS IDOLOS 1 – FROM GENESIS TO REVELATION
SPAIN Decca Records C7827.
Released 1977.
Same as UK 'Rock Roots'.

20. SECONDS OUT
Double album – Live.
UK Charisma GE-2001.
US Atlantic SD2-9002.
EUR Charisma 6641 697.
JAP Charisma SFX 10036-7.
Released October 1977.
All titles composed, arranged and performed by Genesis.
Produced by David Hentschel/Genesis, assisted by Neil Ross.
Recorded in Paris 1976/77 with the

Manor Mobile and mixed at Trident Studios, London.
Front and back sleeve photos by Armando Gallo.
Photography by Armando Gallo, Robert Ellis and Graham Wood.
Cover layout by A&D Design.
Side One: 1. Squonk/2. The Carpet Crawl/3. Robbery, Assault and Battery/ 4. Afterglow.
Side Two: 5. Firth Of Fifth/6. I Know What I Like/7. The Lamb Lies Down On Broadway/8. The Musical Box (Closing Section).
Side Three: 9. Supper's Ready.
Side Four: 10. Cinema Show/ 11. Dance On A Volcano/12. Los Endos.

Tony Banks RMI electric piano, Hammond T. organ, ARP Pro-Soloist, mellotron 400, epiphone 12-string, backing voices. Mike Rutherford Shergold electric 12-string and bass, 8-string bass, Alvarez 12-string, Moog Taurus bass pedals, backing voices. Steve Hackett Gibson Les Paul, Hokada 12-string. Phil Collins voice, Premier and Gretsch drums. Chester Thompson Pearl drums and percussion. Bill Bruford Ludwig and Hayman drums and percussion.

21. . . . AND THEN THERE WERE THREE . . .
UK Charisma CDS 4010.
US Atlantic SD 19173.
EUR Charisma 9124 023.
JAP Charisma RJ7348.
Released April 1978.
All titles arranged and performed by Genesis.
Produced by David Hentschel and Genesis.
Recorded at Relight Studios, Hilvarenbeek, Holland, September 1977.
Mixed at Trident Studios, London, October 1977.

Engineered by David Hentschel, assisted by Steve Short and Pierre Geoffroy Chateau.
Sleeve design and photography by Hipgnosis.
Side One: 1. Down And Out (Collins/ Banks/Rutherford)/2. Undertow (Banks)/ 3. Ballad Of Big (Collins/Banks/ Rutherford)/4. Snowbound (Rutherford)/ 5. Burning Rope (Banks).
Side Two: 6. Deep In The Motherlode (Rutherford)/7. Many Too Many (Banks)/ 8. Scenes From A Night's Dream (Collins/Banks)/9. Say It's Alright Joe (Rutherford)/10. The Lady Lies (Banks)/ 11. Follow You Follow Me (Rutherford/ Banks/Collins).

Tony Banks keyboards. Phil Collins drums, vocals. Mike Rutherford guitar, basses.

22. GENESIS
JAP London Records GXH 1054.
Released 1978.
Same tracks as UK 'Rock Roots'.

ALBUMS

23. THE STORY OF GENESIS
(Double album)
JAP Charisma SFX-10061-2.
Released December 1978.
Japan – only compilation to
commemorate Genesis Tour December
1978.
Front cover and booklet photography
Armando Gallo.
Back cover photo Shintaroh Ichiba.
Album design by Masao Ohgiya.
Includes lyrics in Japanese and English.
    Side One: 1. The Knife/2. The Musical
Box/3. Watcher Of The Skies.
    Side Two: 4. Supper's Ready/5. I
Know What I Like.
    Side Three: 6. The Lamb Lies Down
On Broadway/7. Dance On A Volcano/
8. Squonk/9. Ripples.
    Side Four: 10. Eleventh Earl Of Mar/
11. Your Own Special Way/12. Burning
Rope/13. Follow You Follow Me.

24. NURSERY CRYME/FOXTROT
US Charisma CA-2-2701.
US – only re-release as a double
package.

25. DUKE
UK Charisma CBR 101.
US Atlantic SD 16014.
EUR Charisma 9124 053.
JAP Charisma RJ7655.
Released March 1980.
All titles arranged and performed by
Genesis.
Produced by David Hentschel and
Genesis.
Recorded at Polar Studios, Sweden.
Mixed at Maison Rouge, London.
Engineered by David Hentschel, assisted
by Dave Bascombe.
Sleeve artwork by Lionel Koechlin.
Art direction by Bill Smith.
    Side One: 1. Behind The Lines
(Banks/Collins/Rutherford)/2. Duchess
(Banks/Collins/Rutherford)/3. Guide
Vocal (Banks)/4. Man Of Our Times
(Rutherford)/5. Misunderstanding/
6. Heathaze.
    Side Two: 7. Turn It On Again (Banks/
Collins/Rutherford)/8. Alone Tonight
(Rutherford)/9. Cul-De-Sac (Banks)/
10. Please Don't Ask (Collins)/11. Duke's
Travels (Banks/Collins/Rutherford)/
12. Duke's End (Banks/Collins/
Rutherford).
    Tony Banks keyboards, backing
vocals, 12-string guitar. Mike Rutherford
basses, guitars, backing vocals. Phil
Collins drums, vocals, drum machine.
Dave Hentschel backing vocals.

26. THE SILENT SUN
GER Decca 6.24359.
Released 1980.
Germany – only compilation.
All tracks selected from UK 'Rock Roots'.
    Side One: 1. The Silent Sun/2. That's
Me/3. Fireside Song/4. The Serpent/5. In
The Wilderness.
    Side Two: 6. In Hiding/7. In Limbo/
8. Silent Sun/9. A Place To Call My Own/
10. A Winter's Tale/11. One-Eyed Hound.

Produced by Genesis.
Engineered by Hugh Padgham.
Recorded and mixed at The Farmyard, Surrey.
Sleeve artwork by Bill Smith.
Photograph by Rolf Gobbits.

Side One: 1. Abacab (Banks/Collins/Rutherford)/2. No Reply At All (Banks/Collins/Rutherford)/3. Me And Sarah Jane (Banks)/4. Keep It Dark (Banks/Collins/Rutherford).

Side Two: 5. Dodo (Banks/Collins/Rutherford)/6. Lurker (Banks/Collins/Rutherford)/7. Who Dunnit? (Banks/Collins/Rutherford)/8. Man On The Corner (Collins)/9. Like It Or Not (Rutherford)/10. Another Record (Banks/Collins/Rutherford).

Tony Banks keyboards. Phil Collins drums, vocals. Mike Rutherford basses, guitars. Earth, Wind & Fire horns on 'No Reply At All' courtesy of Earth, Wind & Fire, arranged by Tom Tom 84.

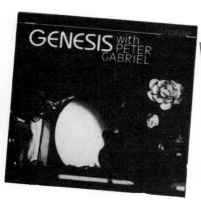

27. GENESIS WITH PETER GABRIEL
GER Decca Profile Series 6.24603.
Germany – only compilation released 1981.
All tracks selected from UK 'Rock Roots'.

Side One: 1. The Silent Sun/2. Where The Sour Turns To Sweet/3. Fireside Song/4. The Serpent/5. Am I Very Wrong?

Side Two: 6. The Conqueror/7. In Hiding/8. One Day/9. Window/10. A Winter's Tale/11. That's Me.

28. ABACAB
UK Charisma CBR 102.
US Atlantic SD-19313.
EUR Vertigo 6302 162.
JAP Vertigo 25PP-32.
Released September 1981 in four different sleeve colour combinations.
All titles arranged and performed by Genesis.

Daryl Stuermer guitar, bass. Chester Thompson drums. Bill Bruford drums and Steve Hackett guitar on 'It/Watcher Of The Skies'.

29. GENESIS BOXED SET
CANADA Atlantic Records.
No special catalogue number.
Limited edition of 2,000.
Includes Selling England By The Pound (KSD 19277), The Lamb Lies Down On Broadway (2SDS-401), A Trick Of The Tail (SD 36-129), Wind And Wuthering (SD 36-144), Seconds Out (2SD-9002), . . . And Then There Were Three . . . (KSD 19173), Spot The Pigeon EP (black vinyl) (EP 1800), Duke (XSD 16014), Abacab (XSD 19313), plus the book 'I Know What I Like' by Armando Gallo, 2 posters and 2 photos.

30. THREE SIDES LIVE
UK Charisma GE 2002.
Released June 1982 in this form for the UK only.
All titles arranged and performed by Genesis.
Produced by Genesis.
Engineered by Geoff Callingham, except for 'Follow You Follow Me'. Side Four engineered by Dave Hentschel courtesy of Dukeslodge Ent.
Sleeve by Bill Smith.
Photograph by Martyn Goddard.
Song-writing credits as for studio recordings.
    Side One: 1. Turn It On Again/ 2. Dodo/3. Abacab.
    Side Two: 4. Behind The Lines/ 5. Duchess/6. Me & Sarah Jane/7. Follow You Follow Me.
    Side Three: 8. Misunderstanding/9. In The Cage (Medley – Cinema Show – Slippermen)/10. Afterglow
    Side Four: 11. One For The Vine/ 12. Fountain Of Salmacis/13. It/Watcher Of The Skies.
    Phil Collins drums, vocals. Tony Banks keyboards, backing vocals. Mike Rutherford guitar, bass, backing vocals.

31. THREE SIDES LIVE
US Atlantic SD 2-2000.
EUR Vertigo 6650 008 (6302 199/200).
Released June 1982 in this form worldwide except UK.
All titles arranged and performed by Genesis.
Produced by Genesis.
Sides 1 - 3 engineered by Geoff Callingham. Song writing credits as for studio recordings.
Side four comprises studio recordings of which tracks 1 - 3 were recorded at The Farm, Surrey, and engineered by Hugh Padgham and Geoff Callingham; tracks 4 & 5 produced by David Hentschel and Genesis.
Sleeve by Bill Smith.
Photograph by Martyn Goddard.

Side One: 1. Turn It On Again/
2. Dodo/3. Abacab.
Side Two: 4. Behind The Lines/
5. Duchess/6. Me & Sarah Jane/7. Follow
You Follow Me.
Side Three: 8. Misunderstanding/9. In
The Cage (Medley – Cinema Show –
Slippermen)/10. Afterglow.
Side Four: 11. Paperlate (Banks/
Collins/Rutherford)/12. You Might Recall
(Banks/Collins/Rutherford)/13. Me And
Virgil (Banks/Collins/Rutherford)/
14. Evidence Of Autumn (Banks)/
15. Open Door (Rutherford).
Phil Collins drums, vocals. Tony
Banks keyboards, backing vocals. Mike
Rutherford guitar, bass, backing vocals.
Sides One to Three only: Daryl Stuermer
guitar, bass. Chester Thompson drums.

32. AND THEN THERE WERE THREE
UK/EUR Compact Disc Charisma
800-059-2.
Released 1983.
Tracks same as standard album
release.

33. ABACAB
UK/EUR Compact Disc Vertigo
800-044-2.
Released 1983.
Tracks same as standard album release.

34. GENESIS
UK Charisma/Virgin GEN LP 1.
US Atlantic 80116-1.
EUR Vertigo. 814 2571.
JAP Vertigo.
Released October 1983.
All songs written by Banks/Collins/
Rutherford.
Produced by Genesis with Hugh
Padgham.
Recorded and mixed at The Farm, Surrey
1983.

Engineered by Hugh Padgham.
Technical assistant Geoff Callingham.
Cover by Bill Smith.
Side One: 1. Mama/2. That's All/
3. Home By The Sea/4. Second Home By
The Sea.
Side Two: 5. Illegal Alien/6. Taking It
All Too Hard/7. Just A Job To Do/
8. Silver Rainbow/9. It's Gonna Get
Better.
Tony Banks keyboards, backing
vocals. Mike Rutherford guitars, bass,
backing vocals. Phil Collins drums,
percussion, lead vocals.

35. GENESIS
UK Compact Disc Charisma/Virgin.
EUR Compact Disc Vertigo 814 287-2.
Released December 1983.
Tracks same as standard album release.

GENESIS
THE LAMB LIES DOWN ON BROADWAY

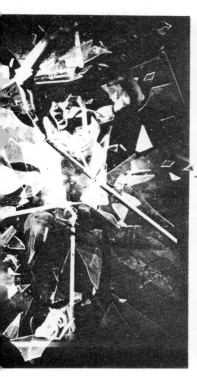

NEW DOUBLE ALBUM
ON CHARISMA CGS 101

OUT NOW!
GENESIS NEW SINGLE CB 238
COUNTING OUT TIME

SOLO EFFORTS

TONY BANKS

1. A CURIOUS FEELING (LP)

UK Charisma CAS 1148.
US Charisma CA-1-2207.
Released October 1979.
Produced by David Hentschel and Tony
Banks.
Engineered by David Hentschel and
Dave Bascombe.
Recorded at Polar Music Studios,
Stockholm.
Mixed at Maison Rouge, London.
Cover painting by Ainslie Roberts

'Wuluwait, The Boatman of the Dead'.
Design by Hothouse.
All tracks written by Tony Banks.
Side One: 1. From The Undertow/
2. Lucky Me/3. The Lie/4. After The Lie/
5.A Curious Feeling/6. Forever Morning.
Side Two: 7. You/8. Somebody Else's
Dream/9. The Waters Of Lethe/10. For A
While/11. In The Dark.

Tony Banks keyboards, guitars, basses, percussion. Kim Beacon vocals. Chester Thompson drums and percussion.

2. FOR A WHILE (Banks)/FROM THE UNDERTOW (Banks) (Single)
UK Charisma CB344.
Released October 1979.
Taken from the album 'A Curious Feeling'.

3. FOR A WHILE (Banks)/FOR A WHILE (Banks) (Single)
US Charisma CA-3503.
Released October 1979.
Double A-side US promo, both sides stereo.
Taken from the album 'A Curious Feeling'.

4. FOR A WHILE (Banks)/A CURIOUS FEELING (Banks) (Single)
UK Charisma CS365 (picture sleeve).
Released July 1980.
A-side is a remixed version.

5. THE SHOUT – FILM SOUNDTRACK
Music not released on record.
Central theme was later to emerge as 'From The Undertow'.

6. THE WICKED LADY – ORIGINAL SOUNDTRACK (LP)
UK Atlantic 78-0073-1.
GER Atlantic U78-00731.
FRANCE Atlantic WE 361.
Released April 1983.
All music composed by Tony Banks. Musical arrangements and orchestration by Christopher Palmer. Side One: Versions of some themes from 'The Wicked Lady' played by Tony Banks. Side Two: Music from 'The Wicked Lady' played by the National Philharmonic Orchestra of London. Recorded at St Peter's Church, Morden, London.
Side One: 1. The Wicked Lady/
2. Spring/3. The Chase/4. Caroline/
5. Jerry Jackson/6. Repentance/
7. Kit/8. Barbara.
Side Two: 9. Prelude to The Wicked Lady/10. Portrait of Jerry Jackson/
11. Caroline's Theme/12. Scherzo/
13. Pastorale/14. The Wicked Lady/
15. Kit's Theme/16. Finale.

7. THIS IS LOVE (Banks)/CHARM (Banks) (Single)
UK Charisma BANKS 1 (812 382-7) (picture sleeve).
Released May 1983.

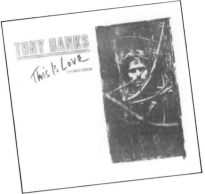

**8. THIS IS LOVE (Extended)
(Banks)/CHARM (Extended)
(Banks) (12" single)**
UK Charisma BANKS 12 (812 382-1)
(picture sleeve).
Released May 1983.

9. THE FUGITIVE (LP)
UK Charisma TBLP 1,
EUR Charisma 812 383-1.
US Atlantic.
Released June 1983.
All songs written by Tony Banks.
Produced by Tony Banks, assisted by
Stephen Short.
Basic tracks recorded at home on
8-track, added to, mixed at, The Farm,
Surrey.
Engineered by Stephen Short.
Technical assistant Geoff Callingham.
Cover by Bill Smith.
Side One: 1. This Is Love/2. Man of
Spells/3. And the Wheels Keep Turning/
4. Say You'll Never Leave Me/5. Thirty-
Threes.

Side Two: 6. By You/7. At The Edge Of
Night/8. Charm/9 Moving Under.
Tony Banks vocals, keyboards, synth
bass, Linn drum. Daryl Stuermer guitars.
Mo Foster bass guitar. Tony Beard, Steve
Gadd, Andy Duncan drums, percussion.

**10. AND THE WHEELS KEEP
TURNING (Banks)/MAN OF SPELLS
(Banks) (Single)**
UK Charisma BANKS 2 (814 216-7)
(picture sleeve).
Released August 1983.

PHIL COLLINS

1. ARK II (Flaming Youth) (LP)
UK Fontana STL 5533.
Released November 1969.
Recorded at De Lane Lea Studios,
London.
Engineered by Barry Ainsworth.
Sleeve concept Barry Saitch.
Photography by Gered Mankowitz.
Stained glass montage by John
Constable.
Side One: 1. Guide Me Orion

(G.Smith)/2. Earthglow (G.Smith/Chatton)/
3. The Planets (Chatton/P.Collins/
G.Smith/Caryl).
 Side Two: 4. Changes (G.Smith/
P.Collins)/5. Pulsar (G.Smith/Chatton)/
6. Space Child (P.Collins)/7. In The Light
Of Love (G.Smith/P.Collins/Chatton/
Caryl)/8. From Now On (Immortal
Invisible) (Chatton).

Phil Collins drums, percussion, vocals.
Gordon Smith guitar, 12-string, bass,
vocal. Ronnie Caryl bass, 12-string, vocal.
Brian Chatton organ, piano, vocal.

2. GUIDE ME ORION (G.Smith)/
FROM NOW ON (IMMORTAL
INVISIBLE) (Chatton)
(Flaming Youth) (Single)
UK Fontana TF1057 (picture sleeve).
Released 1969.

3. EVERY MAN WOMAN AND
CHILD/DRIFTING (Flaming Youth)
(Single)

SPAIN Fontana 6001 002 (picture sleeve).
Released 1969.

4. UNORTHODOX BEHAVIOUR
(Brand X) (LP)
UK Charisma CAS 1117.
US Passport.
Released July 1976.
Recorded at Trident Studios, London,
September/October 1975.
Produced by Brand X and Dennis
Mackay.
Engineered by Dennis Mackay.
Mixed by Dennis Mackay and Robin
Lumley.
Sleeve design by Hipgnosis.
All titles composed by Collins/Goodsall/
Lumley/Jones.
 Side One: 1. Nuclear Burn/
2. Euthanasia Waltz/3. Born Ugly.
 Side Two: 4. Smacks Of Euphoric
Hysteria/5. Unorthodox Behaviour/
6. Running On Three/7. Touch Wood.
 John Goodsall guitars. Percy Jones
basses. Robin Lumley keyboards.
Phil Collins drums, percussion.

SOLO EFFORTS

53

5. MOROCCAN ROLL (Brand X) (LP)
UK Charisma CAS 1126.
US Passport PB 9822.
Released April 1977.
Produced by Dennis Mackay and
Brand X.
Engineered by Steve Tayler.
Recorded at Trident Studios, London,
December 1976/January 1977.
Mixed at Morgan Studios, London
February 1977.
Sleeve design by Hipgnosis/Hardie.
Cover photos by Hipgnosis.
Group photos by Rob Brimson.
Side One: 1. Sun In The Night
(Goodsall)/2. Why Should I Lend You
Mine (When You've Broken Yours Off
Already) . . . into Maybe I'll Lend You
Mine After All (Collins)/3. Hate Zone
(Goodsall)/4. Collapsar (Lumley).
Side Two: 5. Disco Suicide (Lumley/
6. Orbits (Jones)/7. Malaga Virgen
(Jones)/8. Macrocosm (Goodsall).

John Goodsall guitars, backing
vocals. Percy Jones basses, autoharp.
Robin Lumley keyboards, backing
vocals. Phil Collins drums, lead vocals,
acoustic piano. Morris Pert percussion.

6. LIVESTOCK (Brand X) (LP)
(Live recording)
UK Charisma CLASS 5.
US Passport PB9824.
Released November 1977.
Recorded on the Manor Mobile at
Ronnie Scott's Club, London, Septembe
1976, and at Hammersmith Odeon,
London and The Marquee Club, London,
August 1977.
Mixed at Trident Studios, London, August
1977.
Produced by Brand X.
Engineered by Jerry Smith.
Sleeve design and photography by
Hipgnosis.

Side One: 1. Nightmare Patrol
(Goodsall/Dennard/2. -ISH (Goodsall/
Lumley/Jones/Pert/Collins)/3. Euthanasia
Waltz (Goodsall/Jones/Lumley/Collins).
Side Two: 4. Isis Morning,
(i) (Goodsall/Jones/Lumley/Pert/Collins),
(ii) (Collins)/5. Malaga Virgen (Jones).

Phil Collins drums. John Goodsall
guitars. Percy Jones bass. Robin Lumley
keyboards. Morris Pert percussion.
Kenwood Dennard drums on 1 and 4.

7. MASQUES (Brand X) (LP)
UK Charisma CAS 1138.
US Passport PB 9829.
Released September 1978.
Produced by Robin Lumley.
Engineered by Stephen Tayler.
Recorded and mixed at Trident Studios,
London May/June 1978.
Sleeve design layout by AD Design.
Front photo by Chris Kutschera.
Back cover by Hag.
Side One: 1. The Poke/2. Masques
(Jones/Robinson)/3. Black Moon (Pert)/
4. Deadly Nightshade (Pert).
Side Two: 5. Earth Dance (Pert)/
6. Access to Data (Goodsall)/7. The
Ghost Of Mayfield Lodge (Jones).

Percy Jones bass. John Goodsall
guitars. Morris Pert percussion, Fender
piano. Peter Robinson keyboards. Chuck
Burgi drums.

The heavy touring schedule of the
Genesis World Tour 1978 meant that it
was impossible for Phil Collins to take
part in this project. It has been included
here so as to complete the Brand X
listing.

MASQUES

8. PRODUCT (Brand X) (LP)
UK Charisma CAS 1147.
US Passport PB 9840.
Released September 1979.
Produced by Brand X with Colin Green
and Neil Kernon.

Recorded at Startling Studios, Ascot,
England April 1979.
Remixed at Farmyard Studios, Surrey.
Trident Studios, London and Startling
Studios June/July 1979.
'Soho' and 'Wal To Wal' recorded at
'Old Croft', Surrey.
Engineered by Phil Collins.
Sleeve design by Hipgnosis/Colin Elgie.
Photos of Morris and Peter by Paul
Canty, LFI. Photo of Mike Clarke by
John Giblin.
    Side One: 1. Don't Make Waves
(Goodsall)/2. Dance Of The Illegal Aliens
(Jones)/3. Soho (Goodsall/Collins)/4. Not
Good Enough – See Me! (Jones/
Robinson).
    Side Two: 5. Algon (Where An
Ordinary Cup Of Drinking Chocolate
Costs £8,000,000,000) (Lumley)/
6. Rhesus Perplexus (Giblin)/7. Wal To
Wal (Jones/Giblin)/8. . . . And So To F . . .
(Collins)/9. April (Giblin).
    Phil Collins drums, percussion, vocals.
Mike Clarke drums. John Goodsall
guitars, vocals. John Giblin basses.
Robin Lumley keyboards. Morris Pert
percussion. Peter Robinson keyboards,
vocals. Percy Jones basses.

**10. SOHO (Goodsall/Collins)/
DANCE OF THE ILLEGAL ALIENS
(Jones) (Brand X)
(UK 7" single)**
Released September 1979.
B-side should have been 'Noddy Goes
To Sweden' (Jones), however no copies
were released with this B-side.

11. DO THEY HURT? (Brand X) (LP)
UK Charisma CAS 1151.
US Passport PB 9845.
Released May 1980.
Produced by Brand X and Neil Kernon.
Recorded at Startling Studios and
Farmyard Studios, England, at the same
time as the 'Product' album.
Sleeve design and photography by
Hipgnosis, colouring by Richard
Manning.
Liner notes by Michael Palin.
    Side One: 1. Noddy Goes To Sweden
(Jones)/2. Voidarama (Goodsall)/3. Act
Of Will (Goodsall)/4. Fragile! (Jones/
Robinson).

**9. SOHO (Goodsall/Collins)/NODDY
GOES TO SWEDEN (Jones)/POOL
ROOM BLUES (Brand X)
(12" single)**
UK Charisma CB340-12.
Released September 1979.
Phil Collins drums and percussion on
tracks 1 and 3, vocals on track 1.

Side Two: 5. Cambodia (Goodsall)/
6. Triumphant Limp (Goodsall/Giblin/
Lumley/Collins)/7. D.M.Z. (Jones).
Percy Jones bass, vocals. Peter
Robinson keyboards. Phil Collins drums.
John Giblin bass. Robin Lumley
keyboards. John Goodsall guitars.
Mike Clarke drums.

12. IN THE AIR TONIGHT (Collins)/ THE ROOF IS LEAKING (Collins) (Single)
UK Virgin VSK 102 – limited edition with
12-page booklet.
UK Virgin VS 102 (picture sleeve).
US Atlantic 45-3824.
GER Atlantic WEA 79200 (Blue Sleeve)
12".
HOL Atlantic WEA 99143 (B&W Sleeve)
12".
Released January 1981.
Booklet with VSK 102 contains 12
cartoons on Phil's life story by his
brother, Clive Collins.

13. FACE VALUE (LP)
UK Virgin V 2185.
US Atlantic SD 16029.
Produced by Phil Collins, assisted and
engineered by Hugh Padgham.
Recorded at 'Old Croft', Surrey,
Townhouse Studios, London and Village
Recorder, Los Angeles.
Mastered at Sterling Sound, New York.
Sleeve concept, design and titles by Phil
Collins.
All titles composed by Phil Collins except
where noted.
Side One: 1. In The Air Tonight/2. This
Must Be Love/3. Behind The Lines
(Banks/Collins/Rutherford)/4. The Roof
Is Leaking/5. Droned/6. Hand In Hand.
Side Two: 7. I Missed Again/8. You
Know What I Mean/9. Thunder And
Lightning/10. I'm Not Moving/11. If
Leaving Me Is Easy/12. Tomorrow Never
Knows (Lennon/McCartney).
Phil Collins vocals, keyboards, drums,
percussion. Daryl Stuermer guitar, banjo.
John Giblin bass. L. Shankar violins. Joe
Partridge slide guitar. Pete Robinson

keyboards. Ronnie Scott tenor solo. Earth Wind And Fire horns. Stephen Bishop backing vocals. Children Of The Churches Of L.A.

14. I MISSED AGAIN (Collins)/
I'M NOT MOVING (Collins) (Single)
UK Virgin VS 402 (picture sleeve).
UK Virgin VS 402-12 (12″ picture sleeve).
US Atlantic 45-3790.
Released March 1981.

15. IF LEAVING ME IS EASY
(Collins)/DRAWINGBOARD:
i) IN THE AIR TONIGHT (Collins),
ii) I MISSED AGAIN (Collins),
iii) IF LEAVING ME IS EASY (Collins)
(Single)
UK Virgin VS 423 (picture sleeve).
EUR Atlantic WEA 79226 (12″).
Released May 1981.
The three B-side tracks under the title 'Drawingboard' are the original home demo versions of the songs, so are not from the album.
Limited UK edition with poster.

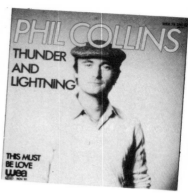

16. I MISSED AGAIN (Collins)/
IN THE AIR TONIGHT (Collins)
(Single)
JAP Atlantic P-1532A (picture sleeve).
Released 1981.

17. THIS MUST BE LOVE (Collins)/
THUNDER AND LIGHTNING (Collins)
(Single)
SPAIN Atlantic 45-2141 (picture sleeve).
Released 1981.

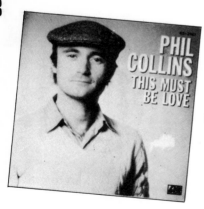

18. THUNDER AND LIGHTNING
(Collins)/THIS MUST BE LOVE
(Collins) (Single)
FRANCE Atlantic/WEA 79260 (picture
sleeve).
Released November 1981.

19. THE SECRET POLICEMAN'S
OTHER BALL – THE MUSIC (LP)
(Various Artistes)
UK Springtime HAHA 6004.
Released March 1982.
Phil Collins performs live 'In The Air
Tonight' and 'The Roof Is Leaking', also
sings in The Secret Police Choir on 'I
Shall Be Released'.
Recorded live at The Secret Policeman's
Other Ball – The 1981 Amnesty
International Benefit Gala at the Theatre
Royal Drury Lane, London September
1981.
Produced by Martyn Lewis.
Sound production by John Strudwick.
Sleeve design by Martyn Lewis and
Graphyk.
Photography by Michael Putland.
A 4-track promo EP has also been
issued.
   Phil Collins piano, vocals. Daryl
Stuermer guitar, banjo.

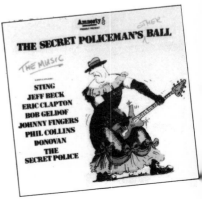

20. IS THERE ANYTHING ABOUT? (Brand X) (LP)

UK CBS CBS 85967.
US Passport Records.
Released September 1982.
Produced by Robin Lumley and Steven Short.
Engineered by Steven Short, Neil Kernon, Colin Green, Craig Milliner.
Recorded incidentally. Mixed at Trident Studios, London.
Sleeve by Bill Smith.
Photography by Andrew Douglas.
    Side One: 1. Ipanaemia (Goodsall)/ 2. A Longer April (Giblin)/3. Modern, Noisy And Effective (Goodsall/Lumley/Short).
    Side Two: 4. Swan Song (Collins/ Lumley/Giblin/Short)/5. Is There Anything About? (Jones/Goodsall/Lumley/Collins)/ 6. TMIU-ATGA (Giblin/Robinson/Lumley).
    Phil Collins drums, percussion. Percy Jones bass. John Giblin bass, Whitbread. Robin Lumley keyboards. Peter Robinson keyboards. John Goodsall guitar. Raf Ravenscroft saxophone. Steven Short syndrums.

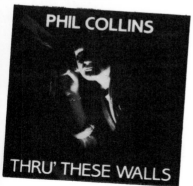

21. THRU' THESE WALLS (Collins)/ DO YOU KNOW, DO YOU CARE (Collins)

Single (picture sleeve)
UK Virgin VS 524 (7")
UK Virgin VSY524 (picdisc 7")
Released October 1982

22. HELLO, I MUST BE GOING! LP

UK Virgin V2252
US Atlantic
Released November 1982
Produced by Phil Collins, assisted by Hugh Padgham.
Engineered by Hugh Padgham, assisted by Howard Gray. Extra mixing on orchestral tracks by Martyn Ford. Recorded at Old Croft, Surrey, over-dubbed at The Farm, Surrey, and Townhouse Studios, London May-June 1982. Strings recorded at CBS Studios, London, engineered by Mike Ross. Main cover photography by Trevor Key. Mastered by Ian Cooper.
All titles composed by Phil Collins except where noted.
    Side One: 1. I Don't Care Anymore/ 2. I Cannot Believe It's True/3. Like China/4. Do You Know, Do You Care?/ 5. You Can't Hurry Love (Holland/Dozier/ Holland).
    Side Two: 6. It Don't Matter To Me/ 7. Thru' These Walls/8. Don't Let Him Steal Your Heart Away/9. The West Side/ 10. Why Can't It Wait 'Til Morning.
    Phil Collins vocals, keyboards, drums, percussion, trumpet. Daryl Stuermer guitars. John Giblin (bass. Mo Foster bass. Peter Robinson keyboards. The Phoenix Horns courtesy E.W.F. Don Myrick, Louis Satterfield, Rhamlee Michael Davis, Michael Harris. The Martyn Ford Orchestra.

23. YOU CAN'T HURRY LOVE
(Holland/Dozier/Holland)/I CANNOT
BELIEVE IT'S TRUE (Collins)
Single (picture sleeve)
UK Virgin VS531 (7")
UK Virgin VS531-12 (12")
UK Virgin VSY 531 (7" picdisc)
Released November 1982.

24. I CANNOT BELIEVE IT'S TRUE
(Collins)/THRU' THESE WALLS
(Collins)
US Atlantic 7-89864 (7"). Single (no
picture sleeve).
Released 1982.

25. TOMATE EL AMOR SIN PRISAS
(YOU CAN'T HURRY LOVE) (Holland/
Dozier/Holland)/I CANNOT
BELIEVE IT'S TRUE (Collins)
SPAIN WEA Records 25 9980-7 (7")
Single (picture sleeve).
Released November 1982.

26. YOU CAN'T HURRY LOVE
(Holland/Dozier/Holland)/I CANNOT
BELIEVE IT'S TRUE (Collins)
JAP WEA P-1736. Single (picture sleeve
with A-side lyrics).
Released January 1983.

27. DON'T LET HIM STEAL YOUR HEART AWAY (Collins)/THUNDER AND LIGHTNING (Collins)
UK Virgin VS572 (7"). Single (picture sleeve).
Released March 1983.
A-side from 'Hello, I Must Be Going!',
B-side from 'Face Value'.

28. DON'T LET HIM STEAL YOUR HEART AWAY (Collins)/AND SO TO F . . . (LIVE) (Collins)
UK Virgin VS572-12 (12"). Single (picture sleeve).
Released March 1983.
B-side by Phil Collins and The Fabulous Jacuzzis, live at Perkins Palace, Pasadena, California.

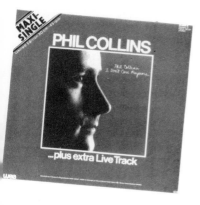

29. I DON'T CARE ANYMORE (Collins)/DON'T LET HIM STEAL YOUR HEART AWAY (Collins)/AND SO TO F . . . (LIVE) (Collins)
GER: WEA Records 25-9935-0 (12").
Single (picture sleeve).

FRANCE: WEA WE 221 (12"). Single (picture sleeve).
Released April 1983.

30. WHY CAN'T IT WAIT 'TIL MORNING (Collins)/LIKE CHINA (Collins)
UK Virgin VS603 (7"). Single (picture sleeve).
Released May 1983.

31. FACE VALUE
UK Compact Disc Virgin CDV 2185,
Released 1983.
Tracks same as standard album release.

32. HELLO, I MUST BE GOING!
UK Compact Disc Virgin CDV 2252,
Released 1983.
Tracks same as standard album release.

SOLO EFFORTS

PHIL COLLINS SESSION WORK

SOLO EFFORTS

**1. OPERATION DAYBREAK
(Film Soundtrack)**

**2. THE SQUEEZE
(Film Soundtrack)**

**3. SEVEN NIGHTS IN JAPAN
(Film Soundtrack)**

5. PETER BANKS (Peter Banks)
Sovereign SVNA 7256.
Released 1973.
Solo album by original Yes guitarist.
(No relation!)

**6. TAKING TIGER MOUNTAIN (BY
STRATEGY) (Eno)**
Island ILPS 9309.
Released 1974.

**7. PETER AND THE WOLF (Various
Artistes)**
RSO 2479 167.
Released 1975.

**4. COLIN SCOTT WITH FRIENDS
(Colin Scott)**
United Artists UAG 29154.
Released 1971.

**8. STARTLING MUSIC (David
Hentschel)**
Ring O'Records 2320 101.
Released 1975.
Instrumental album by one-time Genesis
co-producer.

Philips Norway 6317 041.
Released 1975.
Recorded in Norway whilst on the
Genesis 'Lamb' tour.

15. VOYAGE OF THE ACOLYTE
(Steve Hackett)
Charisma CAS 1111.
Released 1975.
See Steve Hackett section for details.

9. THE EDDIE HOWELL
GRAMOPHONE RECORD (Eddie
Howell)
Warner Bros K56154.
Released 1975.
This session led directly to the formation
of Brand X.

16. MARSCAPE (Various Artistes)
RSO 2394 170.
Released 1976.
Also includes most of Brand X.

17. JOHNNY THE FOX (Thin Lizzy)
Vertigo 9102 012.
Released 1976.

18. BOOK OF FOOLS (Eugene
Wallace)

19. DANGEROUS (Eugene Wallace)

20. JUST ANOTHER STORY FROM
AMERICA (Elliott Murphy)
CBS CBS 81881.
Released 1977.

21. WILLIAM LYALL (William Lyall)
EMI EMA 780.
Released 1977.

22. BEFORE AND AFTER SCIENCE
(Eno)
Island ILPS 9478.
Released 1977.

10. HELEN OF TROY (John Cale)
Island ILPS 9350.
Released 1975.

11. ANOTHER GREEN WORLD (Eno)
Island ILPS 9351.
Released 1975.

12. COUNTERPOINTS (Argent)
RCA RS 1020.
Released 1975.

13. TEASER (Tommy Bolin)
Atlantic K50208.
Released 1975.

14. GI MEG ET HUS (Tobben and
Ero)

23. ROUND THE BACK (Cafe
Jacques)
Epic EPC 82315.
Released 1977.

SOLO EFFORTS

SOLO EFFORTS

**24. THE GEESE AND THE GHOST
(Anthony Phillips)**
Hit & Run Music HIT 001.
Released 1977.
See Anthony Phillips section for details.

25. VIMANA (Nova)
Arista ARTY 138.
Released 1978.

**26. FEELS GOOD TO ME (Bill
Bruford)**
Polydor 2302 075.
Released 1978.

**27. VARIATIONS (Andrew Lloyd
Webber)**
MCA MCF 2824.
Released 1978.

28. MOVING HOME (Rod Argent)
MCA MCF 2854.
Released 1978.

29. EXPOSURE (Robert Fripp)
EG EGLP 101.
Released 1978.

**30. PLEASURE SIGNALS (Wilding
and Bonus)**
Visa IMP 7003.
Released 1978.

31. INTERNATIONAL (Cafe Jacques)
Epic EPC 83042.
Released 1979.

32. I CAN SEE YOUR HOUSE FROM HERE (Camel)
Decca TXS-R 137.
Released 1979.

33. CUTS (John Cale)
Island ILPS 9457.
Released 1979.
Compilation.

34. THE PENTATEUCH OF THE COSMOGONY (Dave Greenslade)
EMI EMSP 332.
Released 1979.

36. QE2 (Mike Oldfield)
Virgin V 2181.
Released 1980.

37. IMMUNITY (Rupert Hine)
A&M AMLH 68519.
Released 1981.

38. GLORIOUS FOOL (John Martyn)
WEA K99178.
Released 1981.
See also under 'Production' section.

39. PLAYING FOR TIME (Chatton)
RCA LP 5058.
Released 1981.
Brian Chatton from 'Flaming Youth'.

SOLO EFFORTS

35. GRACE AND DANGER (John Martyn)
Island ILPS 9560.
Released 1980.

40. LEAD ME TO THE WATER (Gary Brooker)
Mercury 6359 098.
Released 1982.

SOLO EFFORTS

42. SOMETHING'S GOING ON (Frida)
Epic EPC 85966.
Released 1982.

43. PETER GABRIEL (Peter Gabriel)
Charisma CDS 4019.
Released May 1980.

44. THE PRINCIPLE OF MOMENTS (Robert Plant)
Atlantic.
Released 1983.

45. STRIP (Adam Ant)
CBS Records CBS 25705.
Released 1983.
See also under productions section.

41. PICTURES AT ELEVEN (Robert Plant)
Swansong SSK 59418.
Released 1982.

46. IN THE MOOD (Robert Plant)
Es Paranza B6970T.
Released January 1984.
12" single includes Phil Collins on drums on 'Pledge Pin' and 'Horizontal Departure' both live from Dallas, Texas 1983.

MIKE RUTHERFORD

1. BEYOND AN EMPTY DREAM (Various Artistes) (LP)

UK Charisma CAS 1101.
Released 1975.
Includes the hymn 'Take This Heart'
written by Anthony Phillips and Mike
Rutherford, recorded by Charterhouse
Choral Society.
Produced by Anthony Phillips.

5. PRIVATE PARTS AND PIECES II – BACK TO THE PAVILION (Anthony Phillips) (LP)
US Passport PVC 7913.
For details see Anthony Phillips section.

2. VOYAGE OF THE ACOLYTE (Steve Hackett) (LP)
UK Charisma CAS 1111.
For details see Steve Hackett section.

SOLO EFFORTS

6. THE SHOUT (Film Soundtrack)
Music not released on record.
Written with Tony Banks.

7. SMALLCREEP'S DAY (LP)
UK Charisma CAS 1149.
US Passport PB 9843 (Released with
sides 1 and 2 reversed).
Released January 1980.
Produced and engineered by David
Hentschel.
Recorded at Polar Studios, Stockholm.
Mixed at Maison Rouge, London,
assisted by David Bascombe.
Inspired by the book 'Smallcreep's Day'
by Peter Currell-Brown.
Sleeve design and photography by
Hipgnosis.
All titles written by Mike Rutherford.

3. THE GEESE AND THE GHOST (Anthony Phillips) (LP)
UK Hit & Run Music HIT 001.
For details see Anthony Phillips section.

4. PRIVATE PARTS AND PIECES (Anthony Phillips) (LP)
UK Arista Records AFLP 1.
For details see Anthony Phillips section.

Side One: Smallcreep's Day:
1. Between The Tick And The Tock/
2. Working In Line/3. After Hours/4. Cats And Rats (In This Neighbourhood)/
5. Smallcreep Alone/6. Out Into The Daylight/7. At The End Of The Day.

Side Two: 8. Moonshine/9. Time And Time Again/10. Romani/11. Every Road/
12. Overnight Job.

Anthony Phillips keyboards. Noel McCalla vocals. Simon Phillips drums. Morris Pert percussion. Mike Rutherford guitars, basses.

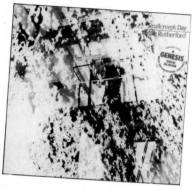

10. MOONSHINE (Rutherford)/ WORKING IN LINE (Rutherford) (Single)
US Passport PS 7919.
Released 1980.
A-side specially remixed for US single release by David Hentschel.

8. WORKING IN LINE (Rutherford)/ COMPRESSION (Rutherford) (Single)
UK Charisma CB353.
Released January 1980.
B-side is not on the album.

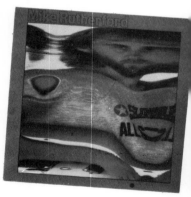

11. HALFWAY THERE (Rutherford/ F.Palmer)/A DAY TO REMEMBER (Rutherford) (Single)
UK WEA K79331 (picture sleeve).
Released August 1982.

12. ACTING VERY STRANGE (LP)
UK WEA K99249.
US Atlantic 8015-1.
JAP WEA P-11275.
Released September 1982.
Produced by Mike Rutherford.
Engineer and assistant producer Nick Launay.
Recorded mainly at The Farm, Surrey, assisted by Geoff Callingham at The Town House, London; The Manor Mobile

9. TIME AND TIME AGAIN (Rutherford)/AT THE END OF THE DAY (Rutherford) (Single)
UK Charisma CB364 (picture sleeve).
Released July 1980.
6,500 copies had 'Overnight Job' as B-side by mistake.

at home.
Cover co-ordinated by Bill Smith.
Photography by Gered Mankowitz.
All songs written by Mike Rutherford
except where noted.

Side One: 1. Acting Very Strange/
2. A Day to Remember/3. Maxine
(Rutherford/Belotte)/4. Halfway There
(Rutherford/F.Palmer).

Side Two: 5. Who's Fooling Who
(Rutherford/F.Palmer)/6. Couldn't Get
Arrested (Rutherford/Belotte)/7. I Don't
Wanna Know/8. Hideaway.

Mike Rutherford vocals, guitars, bass,
keyboards, backing vocals. Daryl
Stuermer guitars. Stewart Copeland
drums. Pete Phipps drums, "The Linn".
Pete Robinson keyboards. Paul Fishman
keyboards. Gary Barnacle sax. Luke
Tunney trumpet. Backing vocals – Steve
Gould, Noel McCalla, Dale Newman.
Strings – arranged and conducted by
Martyn Ford.

13. MAXINE (Rutherford/Bellotte)/
A DAY TO REMEMBER (Rutherford)
Single – picture sleeve
US Atlantic Records
SPAIN WEA Records 79340
Released August 1982.

14. ACTING VERY STRANGE
(Rutherford)/COULDN'T GET
ARRESTED (NIX MIX) (Rutherford/
Bellotte)
Single (picture sleeve)
UK WEA RUTH 1 (25992-7) (7″)
Released October 1982
B-side different from album version.

15. ACTING VERY STRANGE
(EXTENDED) (Rutherford)/
COULDN'T GET ARRESTED
(EXTENDED NIX MIX) (Rutherford/
Bellotte)
Single (picture sleeve)
UK WEA RUTH 1T (25992-0) (12″)

SOLO EFFORTS

Released October 1982
Both sides different from album versions.

Side One: 1. Moribund The Burgermeister/2. Solsbury Hill/3. Modern Love/4. Excuse Me/5. Humdrum.
Side Two: 6. Slowburn/7. Waiting For The Big One/8. Down The Dolce Vita/ 9. Here Comes The Flood.
Peter Gabriel voices, keyboard, flute, recorder. Allan Schwartzberg drums. Tony Levin bass, tuba. Jim Maelem percussion. Steve Hunter guitars. Robert Fripp electric & classical guitar, banjo. Jozef Chirowski keyboards. Larry Fast synthesizers. Dick Wagner backing voice, solo guitar. The London Symphony Orchestra arranged and conducted by Michael Gibbs.

SOLO EFFORTS

16.HIDEAWAY (Rutherford)/ CALYPSO (Rutherford)
UK WEA U-9967. Single (no picture sleeve).
Released January 1983.
B-side non-album track.

PETER GABRIEL

1. PETER GABRIEL (LP)
UK Charisma CDS 4006.
US ATCO SD 36-147.
US Direct Disc Labs/ATCO SD 16615.
EUR Charisma 9103 115.
Released February 1977.
Produced by Bob Ezrin.
Recorded and mixed at The Soundstage, Toronto.
Additional recording at Morgan Studios, Olympic Studios, London.
Sleeve by Hipgnosis.
All songs written by Peter Gabriel except 'Excuse Me' (Gabriel/Martin Hall).

2. SOLSBURY HILL (Gabriel)/ MORIBUND THE BURGERMEISTER (Gabriel) (Single)
UK Charisma CB301 (picture sleeve).
GER Charisma 6073 392.
Released March 1977.

Michael Getlin and Steve Tayler.
Sleeve design and photos by Hipgnosis.
Liner design by Hipgnosis and Colin Elgie.
All tracks written by Peter Gabriel except where noted.
    Side One: 1. On The Air/2. D.I.Y./ 3. Mother Of Violence (Peter & Jill Gabriel)/4. A Wonderful Day In A One-Way World/5. White Shadow.
    Side Two: 6. Indigo/7. Animal Magic/ 8. Exposure (Words Gabriel, Music Fripp/ Gabriel)/9. Flotsam And Jetsam/ 10. Perspective/11. Home Sweet Home.
    Peter Gabriel vocals, organ, piano, synthesizer. Bayete keyboards. Roy Bittan keyboards. Jerry Marotta drums. Tony Levin bass. Sid McGinnis guitars. Robert Fripp guitars, Frippertronics. Larry Fast synthesizers. Timmy Capello saxophone. George Marge recorders.

3. MODERN LOVE (Gabriel)/ SLOWBURN (Gabriel) (Single)
UK Charisma CB302.
Released June 1977.
Also unreleased version with nude Gabriel picture label.

4. D.I.Y. (Gabriel)/PERSPECTIVE (Gabriel) (Single)
UK Charisma CB311 (picture sleeve).
HOL Charisma 6079 462.
Released May 1978.

5. PETER GABRIEL (LP)
UK Charisma CDS 4013.
US ATCO SD 19181.
EUR Charisma 9103 123.
Released June 1978.
Produced by Robert Fripp.
Recorded at Relight Studios, Hilvarenbeek, Holland and The Hit Factory, New York City.
Mixed at The Hit Factory and Trident Studios, London.
Engineered by Steve Short, Ed Sprigg,

6. D.I.Y. (Gabriel)/MOTHER OF VIOLENCE (P&J Gabriel)/ME AND MY TEDDY BEAR (Coots/Winters: re-arranged by Peter Gabriel) (Single)
UK Charisma CB319.
Released September 1978.
'D.I.Y.' is a remixed version, 'Me And My Teddy Bear' is a non-album track.

7. SOLSBURY HILL (Live) (Gabriel) (Single)
UK Charisma SFI-381 (flexidisc).
Recorded live at The Bottom Line, New York, October 4, 1978. Given away free at Hammersmith Odeon, London concerts December 1978, and at a subsequent New York show.

8. GAMES WITHOUT FRONTIERS (Gabriel)/LEAD A NORMAL LIFE (Gabriel) (Single)
US Mercury 76063 (picture sleeve).
Released February 1980.

SOLO EFFORTS

9. GAMES WITHOUT FRONTIERS (Gabriel)/THE START (Gabriel)/ I DON'T REMEMBER (Gabriel) (Single)

UK Charisma CB354 (picture sleeve). Released March 1980.

10. PETER GABRIEL (LP)

UK Charisma CDS 4019.
US Mercury SRM-1-3848.
Released May 1980.
Produced by Steve Lillywhite.
Engineered by Hugh Padgham.
Electronic production by Larry Fast.
Recorded in Bath with the Manor Mobile and at The Townhouse, London.
Sleeve design and photos by Hipgnosis.
All tracks written by Peter Gabriel.
    Side One: 1. Intruder/2. No Self Control/3. Start/4. I Don't Remember/ 5. Family Snapshot/6. And Through The Wire.
    Side Two: 7. Games Without Frontiers/ 8. Not One Of Us/9. Lead A Normal Life/ 10. Biko.
    Peter Gabriel vocals, piano, synthesizers, percussion. Phil Collins drums. Jerry Marotta drums, percussion. Morris Pert percussion. John Giblin bass. Larry Fast bass synthesizer. Tony Levin stick bass. Dick Morrisey saxophone. David Rhodes, Paul Weller, Robert Fripp, Dave Gregory guitars. David Rhodes, Kate Bush backing vocals.

11. NO SELF CONTROL (Gabriel)/ LEAD A NORMAL LIFE (Gabriel) (Single)

UK Charisma CB360 (picture sleeve). Released May 1980,

12. EIN DEUTSCHES ALBUM (LP)

GER Charisma 6302 035.
Released June 1980.
Basically Peter Gabriel (III) re-recorded with German lyrics translated by Horst Königstein.
Produced by Peter Gabriel.
Engineered David Lord and Colin Green at Crescent Studios, Bath, and Trident Studios, London.
Includes three remixed tracks.
All tracks P. Gabriel/H. Königstein.
    Side One: 1. Eindringling/2. Keine

Selbstkontrolle/3. Frag Mich Nicht
Immer/4. Schnappschuss (Ein
Familienfoto)/5. Und Durch Den Draht.
  Side Two: 6. Spiel Ohne Grenzen/
7. Du Bist Nicht Wie Wir/8. Ein Normales
Leben/9. Biko.
  Musicians credits same as Peter
Gabriel (See 10.).

FRANCE Charisma 6000 564 (12"
version, different picture from UK).
Released August 1980.
Produced by Peter Gabriel, engineered
by David Lord.
Tracks 2 and 3 not released on album.

13. SPIEL OHNE GRENZEN (GAMES WITHOUT FRONTIERS) (Gabriel)/JETZT KOMMT DIE FLUT (HERE COMES THE FLOOD) (Gabriel) (Single)

GER Charisma 6000 449 (picture sleeve).
Released June 1980.
Produced by Peter Gabriel
B-side is non-album track.

14. BIKO (Gabriel)/SHOSHOLOZA (Traditional arranged Egnos, Gray & Gabriel)/JETZT KOMMT DIE FLUT (Gabriel) (Single)

UK Charisma CB370 (7" version) (picture
sleeve).
UK Charisma CB370-12 (12" version,
slightly different sleeve from 7").

15. I DON'T REMEMBER (Gabriel)/ SHOSHOLOZA (Traditional arranged Egnos, Gray & Gabriel) (Single)

US Mercury 76086.
Released 1980,
A-side is short version (3.23) from album, B-side is non-album track produced by Peter Gabriel, engineered by David Lord.

16. I DON'T REMEMBER (12″ Limited Edition EP)

CANADA Charisma CEP 303 (picture sleeve).
Released 1980.
Title track from album, others produced by Peter Gabriel, engineered by David Lord.
All tracks Gabriel, except 'Shosholoza' (Traditional arranged Egnos, Gray & Gabriel).
Side One: 1. I Don't Remember/ 2. Shosholoza.
Side Two: 3. Biko (remixed)/4. Jetzt Kommt Die Flut.

17. BRISTOL RECORDER II (Various Artistes)

UK Bristol Recorder BR 002.
Released February 1981.
Magazine format compilation that includes otherwise unreleased Peter Gabriel live material plus 3-page interview.
Not One Of Us (Gabriel) (Live at Leicester 2.80), Humdrum (Gabriel) (Live New York City 7.80), Ain't That Peculiar (Moore/ Robinson/Rogers/Tarplan) (Live Chicago 79).
Peter Gabriel tracks engineered and produced by David Lord.

18. MUSIC AND RHYTHM – A BENEFIT DOUBLE LP FOR A WORLD OF MUSIC ARTS AND DANCE

UK WEA K68045.
Released July 1982, to assist with funds for the WOMAD Festival.
Includes 'Across The River' (Gabriel/ Shankar/Rhodes/Copeland).
Produced by Peter Gabriel and David Lord at Shabby Road Studios and Crescent Studios, Bath.

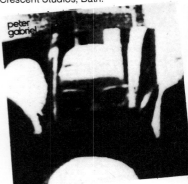

19. PETER GABRIEL
LP

UK Charisma PG4
US Geffen Records, additional title 'Security'.
Released September 1982.
Produced by David Lord and Peter Gabriel.
Electronic production and processing by Larry Fast and Peter Gabriel.
Engineered by David Lord, assisted by Neil Perry.
Recorded 'At Home' (first two weeks with Mobile One), mixed at Crescent Studios, Bath. Remix of 'Shock The Monkey' at Sarm Studios, London, engineered by Julian Mendelsohn and Danny Heaps.
Digital editing at Advision Studios, London, with Mike King.
Artwork based on video images by Malcolm Poynter, Peter Gabriel and David Gardner.
All songs written by Peter Gabriel.
Side One: 1. Rhythm Of The Heat/
2. San Jacinto/3. I Have The Touch/
4. The Family And The Fishing Net.
Side Two: 5. Shock The Monkey/
6. Lay Your Hands On Me/7. Wallflower/
8. Kiss Of Life.

Peter Gabriel vocals, CMI, Linn programming, drums, Prophet, backing vocals, vocal noises. Jerry Marotta drums. Tony Levin bass, stick, fretless bass. Larry Fast Moog, Moog brass and electronic percussion, Prophet. David Rhodes guitars, backing vocals. John Ellis guitars, backing vocals. Roberto Laneri treated sax. Morris Pert percussion. Contributions also from Stephen Paine, David Lord, Peter Hammill, Jill Gabriel, Ekome Dance Company.

20. SHOCK THE MONKEY (Gabriel)/ "SOFT DOG" (INSTRUMENTAL) (Gabriel)

Single (picture sleeve)
UK Charisma SHOCK 1 (7")
UK Charisma SHOCK 12 (12")
UK Charisma SHOCK 122 (7" picdisc)
Released 6th September 1982.
B-side non-album track.

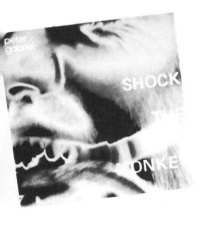

21. I DON'T REMEMBER (Gabriel)/ NO SELF CONTROL (Gabriel)

Single (picture sleeve)
HOL Charisma 6000 661 (7")
Released October 1982

22. SCHOCK DEN AFFEN (Gabriel)/ SOFT DOG (INSTRUMENTAL) (Gabriel)

Single (picture sleeve)
GER Charisma 6000 876 (7")

SOLO EFFORTS

SOLO EFFORTS

23. PETER GABRIEL – DEUTSCHES ALBUM
LP
GER Charisma 6302 221
Released November 1982. Credits as for 19 (PG4).
All songs written by Peter Gabriel, lyrics by Peter Gabriel and Horst Konigstein.
   Side One: 1. Der Rhythmus Der Hitze/ 2. Das Fischernetz/3. Kon-Takt!/4. San Jacinto.
   Side Two: 5. Schock Den Affen/ 6. Handauflegen/7. Nicht Die Erde Hat Dich Verschlukt/8. Mundzumund-beatmung.

24. I HAVE THE TOUCH (Gabriel)/ ACROSS THE RIVER (Gabriel/ Shankar/Rhodes/Copeland)
Single (picture sleeve)
UK Charisma CB405 (7″)
Released December 1982.

25. SOLSBURY HILL (Gabriel)/ GAMES WITHOUT FRONTIERS (Gabriel)
UK Old Gold Records OG-9265
(no picture sleeve).
Released January 1983.
Re-release of two original A-sides.

26. PETER GABRIEL PLAYS LIVE (LP)
UK Charisma PGDL 1.
EUR Charisma 812 445-1.
US Geffen 2GHS 4012.
All songs written by Peter Gabriel.
Produced by Peter Gabriel and Peter Walsh.
Recorded by Le Mobile on Autumn 1982 Tour of the United States and Canada.
Live recording engineered by Neil Kernon.
Fix 'n' mix at Shabbey Road Studios, Bath, Spring 1983.
Engineered by Peter Walsh.
Digitally mastered by Peter Wolliscroft.

Sleeve photography by Armando Gallo and Margaret Maxwell.
 Side One: 1. The Rhythm Of The Heat/ 2. I Have The Touch/3. Not One Of Us/ 4. Family Snapshot.
 Side Two: 5. D.I.Y./6. The Family And The Fishing Net/7. Intruder/8. I Go Swimming.
 Side Three: 9. San Jacinto/ 10. Solsbury Hill/11. No Self Control/ 12. I Don't Remember.
 Side Four: 13. Shock The Monkey/ 14. Humdrum/15. On The Air/16. Biko.
 Peter Gabriel vocals, synthesizer, piano. David Rhodes guitar, backing vocals. Tony Levin stick, bass, backing vocals. Larry Fast synthesizer, piano. Jerry Marotta drums, percussion, backing vocals.

27. I DON'T REMEMBER (LIVE– REMIX) (Gabriel)/SOLSBURY HILL (LIVE) (Gabriel) (Single)
UK Charisma GAB 1 (picture sleeve). Released June 1983.

28. I DON'T REMEMBER (LIVE– REMIX) (Gabriel)/SOLSBURY HILL (LIVE) (Gabriel)/KISS OF LIFE (LIVE) (Gabriel) (12″ single)
UK Charisma GAB12 (812 833-1) (picture sleeve).
Released June 1983.
'Kiss Of Life' (Live) is not included on album.
Initial copies with free limited edition white label 12″ GAB 122 with 'Games Without Frontiers' (Gabriel) and 'Schnappschuss' (Family Snapshot sung in German) (Gabriel).

29. SOLSBURY HILL (LIVE) (Gabriel)/I GO SWIMMING (LIVE) (Gabriel) (Single)
US Geffen 7-29542 (no picture sleeve). Released June 1983.

30. PETER GABRIEL (4)
EUR Compact Disc 800-091-2 Charisma. Released 1983.
Tracks same as standard album release.

PETER GABRIEL SESSION WORK

SOLO EFFORTS

1. MONA BONE JAKON (Cat Stevens) (LP)
Island ILPS 9118.
Released 1970.
Peter Gabriel played flute on 'Kathmandu' track.

2. COLIN SCOTT WITH FRIENDS (Colin Scott) (LP)
United Artists UAG 29154.
Visa IMP 1009.
Released 1971.
Includes Peter Gabriel.

SOLO EFFORTS

3. ALL THIS AND WORLD WAR I (Various Artistes) (LP)
Riva RVLP 2 (UK double album)
20th Century 2T-522 (US boxed double).
A film soundtrack of World War II film
footage, linked to Beatles' songs
performed by various artistes. Includes
'Strawberry Fields Forever' by Peter
Gabriel.

4. EXPOSURE (Robert Fripp) (LP)
EG EGLP 101.
Released 1978.
Includes Peter Gabriel vocals, tracks
'Here Comes The Flood' (Gabriel) and
'Exposure' (Fripp/Gabriel).

5. FOUR FROM EXPOSURE (Robert Fripp) (12″ promo EP)
EG Records.
Released 1978.
Includes 'Here Comes The Flood',
'Exposure'.

6. CHORDS (Synergy) (LP)
Passport PB6000.
Released 1978.
Synergy is Larry Fast, regular contributor
to Peter Gabriel recordings and live work.
Gabriel helped with song titles.

7. WALKING INTO MIRRORS (Johnny Warman) (LP)
Rocket TRAIN 17.
Vocals by Gabriel on one track.

STEVE HACKETT

1. THE ROAD (Quiet World) (LP)
UK Dawn DNIS 3007.
Released 1970.
1. The Great Birth/2. Theme/3. First
Light/4. Theme/5. Star/6. Theme/
7. Loneliness/8. Theme/9. Change Of
Age/10. Christ One/11. Hang On/
12. Christ Continued/13. Body To The
Mind/14. Traveller/15. Let Everybody
Sing/16. Theme/17. Children Of The
World/18. Change Of Age/19. Love Is
Walking.

Steve played guitar in Quiet World
before he joined Genesis.

2. LOVE IS WALKING/CHILDREN OF THE WORLD (Quiet World) (Single)
UK Dawn 1970.

3. PETER BANKS (Peter Banks) (LP)
UK Sovereign SVNA 7256.
Released 1973.
Solo album by original Yes guitarist, includes Steve Hackett on guitar.

4. VOYAGE OF THE ACOLYTE (LP)
UK Charisma CAS 1111.
US Chrysalis CHR 1112.
Released October 1975.
Produced by Steve Hackett/John Acock.
Engineered by John Acock.
Recorded at Kingsway Recorders, London, June/July 1975.
Album cover paintings by Kim Poor.
All titles composed and arranged by Steve Hackett, apart from collaboration as noted.

Side One: 1. Ace Of Wands/2. Hands Of The Priestess Part 1/3. A Tower Struck Down (S.Hackett/John Hackett)/ 4. Hands Of The Priestess Part II/ 5. The Hermit.

Side Two: 6. Star Of Sirius/7. The Lovers/8. Shadow Of The Hierophant (S.Hackett/M.Rutherford).

Steve Hackett electric and acoustic guitars, mellotron, harmonium, bells, autoharp, vocal, effects. John Hackett flute, ARP synthesizer, bells. Mike Rutherford bass guitar, bass pedals, fuzz 12-string. Phil Collins drums, vibes, percussion, vocals. John Acock Elka Rhapsody, mellotron, harmonium, piano. Sally Oldfield vocal. Robin Miller oboe, cor anglais. Nigel Warren-Green solo cello. Percy Jones extra bass on 'Tower'. John Gustafson bass on 'Star'. Steve Tobin parrot and cough!

5. STAR OF SIRIUS (Hackett) (mono)/STAR OF SIRIUS (Hackett) (stereo) (Single)
US Chrysalis PRO 633.
US double A-side promo 1976.

SOLO EFFORTS

6. PLEASE DON'T TOUCH (LP)

UK Charisma CDS 4012.
US Chrysalis CHR 1176.
EUR Charisma 9124 024.
Released April 1978.
Produced by John Acock/Steve Hackett.
Recorded between November 1977 and
February 1978 at Kingsway Studios,
London De Lane Lea Studios, London,
Cherokee Studios, Record Plant, Los
Angeles.
Engineered by John Acock.
Cover illustration by Kim Poor.
Sleeve design Kim Poor and A.D. Design.
Photography by John Brown and
Armando Gallo.
All songs composed and arranged by
Steve Hackett.
    Side One: 1. Narnia/2. Carry On Up
The Vicarage/3. Racing In A/4. Kim/
5. How Can I?
    Side Two: 6. Hoping Love Will Last/
7. Land Of A Thousand Autumns/
8. Please Don't Touch/9. The Voice of
Necam/10. Icarus Ascending.
    Steve Hackett electronic and acoustic
guitars, keyboards, vocals, percussion.
John Hackett flutes, piccolos, bass
pedals, keyboards. John Acock
keyboards. Dave Lebolt keyboards.
Richie Havens vocals, percussion.
Randy Crawford vocals. Chester
Thompson drums, percussion. Phil Ehart
drums, percussion. Steve Walsh vocals.
James Bradley percussion.

7. HOW CAN I? (Hackett)/KIM (Hackett) (Single)

UK Charisma CB312.
GER Charisma 6079 463 (picture sleeve).
HOL Charisma 6079 463 (picture sleeve).
Released May 1978.
Taken from the album 'Please Don't
Touch'.

8. NARNIA (Hackett)/PLEASE DON'T TOUCH (Hackett) (Single)

UK Charisma CB318.
Released October 1978.
A-side is a remixed version.

9. NARNIA (Hackett)/KIM (Hackett) (Single)

US Chrysalis CHS-2237.
Released 1978.
A-side is a remixed version.

10. SPECTRAL MORNINGS (LP)

UK Charisma CDS 4017.
US Chrysalis CHR 1223.
Released May 1979.
Produced by John Acock/Steve Hackett.
Recorded at Phonogram Studios,
Hilversum, Holland.
Front cover by Kim Poor.
Sleeve design by Cooke-Key.
Photography by Tom Sheehan.
All titles written by Steve Hackett.
    Side One: 1. Every Day/2. The Virgin
And The Gypsy/3. The Red Flower Of
Tachai Blooms Everywhere/4. Clocks –

The Angel Of Mons/5. The Ballad Of The Decomposing Man.

Side Two: 6. Lost Time In Cordoba/ 7. Tigermoth/8. Spectral Mornings.

Steve Hackett guitars, Roland Guitar Synthesizer, Koto, harmonica, vocals, extras. Pete Hicks lead vocals and harmonies. Dik Cadbury bass, bass pedals, violin, vocals. Nick Magnus keyboards. John Hackett flutes, bass pedals. John Shearer drums and percussion.

11. EVERY DAY (Hackett)/LOST TIME IN CORDOBA (Hackett) (Single)
UK Charisma CB334.
Released June 1979.
A-side is a re-recorded version.

12. CLOCKS – THE ANGEL OF MONS (Hackett)/ACOUSTIC SET (Includes excerpts from Lost Time In Cordoba; Traditional Guitar Exercise; Blood On The Rooftops; Horizons; Kim) (Hackett) (Single)
UK Charisma CB341.
Released September 1979.
A-side is a remixed version, B-side not on the album.
Recorded live at the Pavilion de Paris 11th June 1979.
Musicians as for 'Spectral Mornings'.

13. CLOCKS – THE ANGEL OF MONS (Hackett)/ACOUSTIC SET (Includes excerpts from Lost Time In Cordoba; Traditional Guitar Exercise; Blood On The Rooftops; Horizons; Kim) (Hackett)/ TIGERMOTH (LAY DOWN YOUR ARMS AND SURRENDER TO MINE Pt.1) (Hackett) (12" Single)
UK Charisma CB341-12 (picture sleeve).
Released September 1979.
A-side is a remixed version, B-side not on the album.

Recorded live at the Pavilion de Paris 11th June 1979.
Musicians as for 'Spectral Mornings'.

14. DEFECTOR (LP)
UK Charisma CDS 4018.
US Charisma Records.
Released June 1980.
Produced by John Acock and Steve Hackett.
Recorded at Wessex Studios, Highbury, London.
Inside and cover enamels by Kim Poor.
Design by Kim and Kobz.
Collage photos by Armando Gallo, Gered Mankowitz, Jack Nouws, and friends.
Limited edition poster with initial copies.
All tracks written by Steve Hackett except where noted.

Side One: 1. The Steppes/2. Time To Get Out/3. Slogans/4. Leaving/5. Two Vamps As Guests.

Side Two: 6. Jacuzzi/7. Hammer In The Sand/8. The Toast/9. The Show/

10. Sentimental Institution (S.Hackett/
P.Hicks).
    Steve Hackett guitar, vocal, Optigan,
Roland GR500. Nick Magnus keyboards.
John Hackett concert and alto flute.
Pete Hicks vocal. John Shearer drums,
percussion. Dik Cadbury bass, vocal.

15. THE SHOW (Hackett)/
HERCULES UNCHAINED (Hackett)
(Single)
UK Charisma CB357 (picture sleeve).
Released March 1980.
B-side not included on the album.

steve hackett

CURED

16. SENTIMENTAL INSTITUTION
(Hackett/Hicks)/THE TOAST
(Hackett) (Single)
UK Charisma CB368 (picture sleeve).
Released August 1980.
Both tracks taken from 'Defector'.

17. CURED (LP)
UK Charisma CDS 4021.
US Epic ARE 37632.
Released August 1981.
Produced by Steve Hackett, John Acock

and Nick Magnus.
Engineered by John Acock.
Recorded at Redan Studios, Los Angeles.
Cover photos by Kim Poor.
Design by Bryan Hemming and
Kim Poor.
Photo by Armando Gallo.
All titles written by Steve Hackett except
where noted.
    Side One: 1. Hope I Don't Wake/
2. Picture Postcard/3. Can't Let Go/4. The
Air-Conditioned Nightmare.
    Side Two: 5. Funny Feelings
(S.Hackett/Magnus)/6. A Cradle Of
Swans/7. Overnight Sleeper (S.Hackett/
Poor)/8. Turn Back Time.
    Steve Hackett guitars, bass, vocals.
Nick Magnus keyboards, drum machine.
Bimbo Acock saxophone. John Hackett
flute, bass pedals.

18. HOPE I DON'T WAKE (Hackett)/
TALES OF THE RIVERBANK (Anon.)
(Single)
UK Charisma CB365 (picture sleeve).
Released August 1981.
B-side not included on the album.

steve hackett

SOLO EFFORTS

19. PICTURE POSTCARD (Hackett)/ THEME FROM 'SECOND CHANCE' (Hackett) (Single)
UK Charisma CB 390.
Released October 1981.
B-side is the theme Steve wrote for the ITV series 'Second Chance'. It features Steve Hackett acoustic guitars. John Hackett flute.

20. CELL 151 (Hackett)/TIME LAPSE AT MILTON KEYNES (Hackett) (Single)
UK Charisma CELL 1 (811 341-7) (picture sleeve).
Released April 1983.

21. CELL 151 (Hackett)/AIR CONDITIONED NIGHTMARE (LIVE) (Hackett)/TIME LAPSE AT MILTON KEYNES (Hackett) (12" Single)
UK Charisma CELL 12 (811 341-1). (picture sleeve).
Released April 1983.
Initial copies with free limited edition white label 12" of 'Clocks' CB341-12.

22. HIGHLY STRUNG (LP)
UK Charisma HACK 1.
EUR Charisma 811 209-1.
Released April 1983.
Produced by Steve Hackett and John Acock.
Recorded in London at Berry Street Studios, Marcus Music & Redan Recorders February to November 1982.
Engineered by John Acock, Rafe McKenna, Brad Grisdale, assisted by Bob Kraushaar.
Mastered by Kevin Metcalfe at Utopia Studios, London.
Front and back paintings by Kim Poor.
   Side One: 1. Camino Royale (Hackett/Magnus)/2. Cell 151 (Hackett)/ 3. Always Somewhere Else (Hackett)/ 4. Walking Through Walls (Hackett).
   Side Two: 5. Give It Away (Hackett)/ 6. Weightless (Hackett)/7. Group Therapy (Hackett)/8. India Rubber Man (Hackett)/ 9. Hackett to Pieces (Hackett/Magnus).
   Steve Hackett guitars, vocals. Nick Magnus keyboards, devices. Ian Mosley drums. Nigel Warren-Green cello. Chris Lawrence contrabass.

23. BAY OF KINGS (LP)
UK Lamborghini Records IMG LP 3000.
Released November 1983.
Produced by Steve Hackett and John Acock.
Recorded at Berry Street and the Townhouse, London.
Mastered by Kevin Metcalfe at Utopia Studios, London.
Front cover by Kim Poor, photo by Steve Morhan.
All titles by Steve Hackett.
   Side One: 1. Bay Of Kings/2. The Journey/3. Kim (re-arranged version)/ 4. Marigold/5. St Elmo's Fire.
   Side Two: 6. Petropolis/7. Second Chance/8. Cast Adrift/9. Horizons/

10. Black Light/11. The Barren Land/
12. Calmaria.
   Steve Hackett acoustic guitar,
keyboard, strings. John Hackett flutes.
Nick Magnus keyboard, strings, effects.

SOLO EFFORTS

ANTHONY PHILLIPS

1. BEYOND AN EMPTY DREAM (Various Artistes) (LP)
UK Charisma CAS 1101.
Released 1975.
Includes the hymn 'Take This Heart'
written by Anthony Phillips and Mike
Rutherford, recorded by Charterhouse
Choral Society.
Produced by Anthony Phillips.

2. THE GEESE AND THE GHOST (LP)
UK Hit And Run Music HIT 001.
US Passport PP98020.
US PVC PVC 8905 (re-released end
1981).
Released March 1977.
Produced and engineered by Simon
Hayworth, Michael Rutherford and
Anthony Phillips.
Recorded at Send Barnes Studios,
Argonaut Galleries, Surrey.
Remixed and completed at Trident
Studios, London and Olympic Studios,
London.
Cover design and art by Peter Cross.
   Side One: 1. Wind – Tales (Phillips)/
2. Which Way The Wind Blows (Phillips)/
3. Henry; Portraits From Tudor Times:
(i) Fanfare, (ii) Lute's Chorus, (iii) Misty
Battlements, (iv) Henry Goes To War,
(v) Death Of A Knight, (vi) Triumphant
Return (Phillips/Rutherford)/4. God If I
Saw Her Now (Phillips).
   Side Two: 5. Chinese Mushroom
Cloud (Phillips/Rutherford)/6. The Geese
And The Ghost (Part i, Part ii) (Phillips/
Rutherford)/7. Collections (Phillips)/
8. Sleepfall: The Geese Fly West (Phillips).
   Anthony Phillips acoustic 12-string,
6-string, classical guitar, electric 6- and
12-string guitars, basses, dulcimer,
guitar, bazouki, synthesizers, mellotron,
harmonium, piano, organ, celeste, pin
piano, drums, glockenspiel, timbales,
bells and chimes, gong, vocal on

'Collections'. Michael Rutherford acoustic 12-string, 6-string, classical guitars, electric 6- and 12-string guitars, basses, organ, drums, timbales, glockenspiel, cymbals, bells. Phil Collins vocals on 'Which Way The Wind Blows' and 'God If I Saw Her Now'. Other contributions by Rob Phillips, Lazo Momulovich, John Hackett, Wil Sleath, Jack Lancaster, Charlie Martin, Kirk Trevor, Nick Hayley, Martin Westlake, Tom Newman, Viv McCauliffe, Send Barnes Orchestra and Barge Rabble conducted by Jeremy Gilbert, Ralph Bernascone soloist!

What (Are They Doing To My Little Friends?).

Anthony Phillips vocals, harmonica. Michael Giles drums. John G. Perry Wal custom bass. The Vicar guitars, keyboards, sundries. Jeremy Gilbert keyboards on 'Greenhouse', harp on 'Now What'. Mel Collins soprano saxophone, flute. Rupert Hine percussion, backing vocals, locks, probs, modes and vibes. Perkin Alanbeck synthesizer. Humbert Ruse and Vic Stench drums and bass on 'Greenhouse'. Rodent Rabble clicks, claps and crampons!

3. IGTB (Intergalactic Touring Band) (LP)
UK Charisma CDS 4009.
Released November 1977.
Concept project put together by Marty Scott of Passport Records.
Includes Anthony Phillips on guitars.

4. WISE AFTER THE EVENT (LP)
UK Arista SPART 1063.
US Passport PB 9828 (and picture disc PB 9828).
EUR Vertigo 9124 361.
Released June 1978.
Produced by Rupert Hine.
Recorded at Essex Studios, London, October 1977, and the Manor Mobile at the 'Farmyard' Nov./Dec. 1977.
'Regrets' recorded at CBS Studios, London, December 1977.
Mixed at Trident Studios, London, Dec.77/Jan.78
Designs and artwork by Peter Cross.
All titles composed by Anthony Phillips except 'Greenhouse' (Gilbert/Phillips).
Side One: 1. We're All As We Lie/ 2. Birdsong/3. Moonshooter/4. Wise After The Event.
Side Two: 5. Pulling Faces/6. Regrets/ 7. Greenhouse/8. Paperchase/9. Now

5. WE'RE ALL AS WE LIE (Phillips)/ SQUIRREL (Phillips)/SITARS AND NEBULOUS (Phillips) (Single)
UK Arista ARIST 192.
Released June 1978.
B-side tracks not on the album.
Robin Phillips oboe on 'Sitars and Nebulous'.

SOLO EFFORTS

6. SQUIRREL (Phillips)/SITARS AND NEBULOUS (Phillips) (Single)
US Passport PS 7914.
Released 1978.

7. PRIVATE PARTS AND PIECES: A COLLECTION OF GUITAR AND PIANO SOLOS, DUETS AND ENSEMBLES 1972-1976 (LP)
US Passport/PVC PVC 7905.
Released January 1979.
UK Arist AFLP 1.
Limited edition of 5,000 issued as double-pack with 'Sides', after which it was deleted.
Released March 1979.
Produced by Anthony Phillips, except 'Tibetan Yak-Music' produced by Harry Williamson.
Recorded at Send Barnes, Surrey.
Remixed by Ray Staff at Trident Studios, London.
Mastered at Trident Studios, London, August 1978.
Cover design and art by Peter Cross.
All titles written by Anthony Phillips, except 'Field Of Eternity' (Phillips/Rutherford).
Side One: 1. Beauty And The Beast/
2. Field Of Eternity/3. Tibetan Yak-Music/
4. Lullaby – Old Father Time/
5. Harmonium In The Dust (Or Harmonious Stratosphere)/6. Tregenna Afternoons. (HOME SIDE)
Side Two: 7. Reaper/8. Autumnal/
9. Flamingo/10. Seven Long Years. (AWAY SIDE)
Anthony Phillips guitars, keyboards.

8. SIDES (LP)
UK Arista SPART 1085 (first 5,000 included No.7 above).
US Passport PB 9843.
Released March 1979.
Produced by Rupert Hine.
Recorded at Essex Studios, London, October 1978.

Engineered by Richard Austin, Andy Pierce; and at Matrix Studios, England, November 1978, engineered by Nick Bradford.
Mixed at Trident Studios, London, Nov./Dec. 1978.
Conceived between Send Barns and Golborne Road, Aug./Sept. 1978.
Artwork by Peter Cross.
Photography by Robert Ellis.
All titles composed by Anthony Phillips.
Side One: (FIRST HALF) 1. Um & Aargh/2. I Want Your Love/3. Lucy Will/4. Side Door/5.* Holy Deadlock.
Side Two: (SECOND HALF) 6. Sisters Of Remindum/7. Bleak House/.
8. Magdalen/9. Nightmare.
*Lyrics by Martin Hall.
Anthony Phillips guitars, keyboards. The Vicar vocals. Mike Giles drums. John G. Perry bass. Dale Newman vocals. Dan Owen vocals. Ray Cooper, Frank Ricotti, Morris Pert percussion. Mel Collins tenor saxophone.

9. UM & AARGH (Phillips)/
SOUVENIRS (Phillips) (Single)
UK Arista ARIST 252 (picture sleeve)
Released April 1979.
B-side non-album track.

10. PRIVATE PARTS AND PIECES II
– BACK TO THE PAVILION (LP)
UK – No release.
US PVC PVC 7913.
Released June 1980.
'Scottish Suite' recorded at Send Barns,
Surey and Olympic Studios, London,
June 1976, produced by Anthony Phillips
and Anton Matthews.
Tracks 7,8,10,12 recorded at Essex
Studios, London, the Farmyard, Surrey,
and Trident Studios, London, Nov./Dec.
1977.
Produced by Rupert Hine.
The rest recorded at Slick Sound in the
North Sea on the vicar's mobile oil rig
ten and sponsored by Ralph
Bernascone Aquasports Ltd!
Cover design by Peter Cross.
All titles composed by Anthony Phillips.
  Side One: (N.O.R. SIDE) 1. Scottish
Suite (A collection of Scottish salmon
farmers' songs and 12th century
Paraguayan tin-miner's threnodies):
(i) Salmon Leap, (ii) Parting Thistle,
(iii) Electric Reaper, (iv) Amorphous,
Cadaverous And Nebulous, (v) Salmon's
Last Sleepwalk./2. Lindsay/3. K2/
4. Postlude: End Of The Season.
  Side Two: (S.O.R. SIDE) 5. Heavens/
6. Spring Meeting/7. Romany's Aria/
8. Chinaman/9. Nocturne/10. Magic
Garden/11. Von Runkel's Yorker Music/
12. Will O! The Wisp/13. Tremulous/
14. I Saw You Today/15. Back To The
Pavilion.
  Anthony Phillips all instruments,
except Andy McCulloch drums and
percussion. Mike Rutherford bass on
'Scottish Suite' (i), (iv). Rob Phillips oboe
on 'Von Runkel's Yorker Music'. Mel
Collins flute on 'Tremulous'.

11. MIKE RUTHERFORD –
SMALLCREEP'S DAY (LP)
UK Charisma CAS 1149.
For details see Mike Rutherford section.

SOLO EFFORTS

12. 1984 (LP)
UK RCA RCA LP 5036.
US Passport Records.
Released July 1981.
Produced and engineered by Anthony
Phillips assisted by Richard Scott.
8-track recorded at Send Barnes, Surrey,
August 1980 to January 1981.
Completed, mixed at Atmosphere
Studios, London February to March 1981.
Engineered by Chris David.
Vocoder manipulated by Chris and Anita
David.
Cover design by Under The Stairs
Productions.
All tracks written and arranged by
Anthony Phillips.
  Side One: 1. Prelude '84/2. 1984
Part 1.
  Side Two: 3. 1984 Part 2/4. Anthem
1984.

Anthony Phillips keyboards, Roland CR78 drumbox, occasional guitar, basic percussion. Richard Scott basic percussion, effects, vocal ideas. Morris Pert percussion- timps, tambourine, gong, congas, bell-tree, vibra-slap, marimbas, vibes, etc.

SOLO EFFORTS

13. PRELUDE '84 (Phillips)/ ANTHEM 1984 (Phillips) (Single)
UK RCA RCA 102 (picture sleeve).
Released July 1981.
Both tracks taken from '1984'.

14. PRIVATE PARTS AND PIECES III – ANTIQUES (Anthony Phillips and Enrique Berro Garcia) (LP)
UK – RCA International INT 5228.
US PVC PVC 8908.
Released March 1982.
Produced by Anthony Phillips.
Recorded at Send Barns, Surrey, June 1981.
Mixed by Chris David at Atmosphere Studios, London, August 1981.
Album sleeve by Peter Cross.
All titles by Phillips/Berro Garcia except

'Ivied Castles' and 'Old Wives Tales' by Phillips.
Side One: 1. Motherforest/
2. Hurlingham Suite: (i) Ivied Castles, (ii) Frosted Windows, (iii) Bandido, (iv) Church Bells At Sunset/3. Suite In D Minor: (i) Whirlpools, (ii) Cobblestones, (iii) Catacombs.
Side Two: 4. Danse Nude/
5. Esperanza/6. Elegy/7. Otto's Face/
8. Sand Dunes/9. Old Wives Tale.
Anthony Phillips classical 12-, 6-string guitars, bass guitar. Enrique Berro Garcia classical, 12-string guitars, electric guitar.

15. THE SINGLE FACTOR (Camel) (LP)
UK Decca SKL 5328.
Released May 1982.
Anthony Phillips plays on 'Heroes', 'Selva', 'Sasquatch', 'Manic', and 'End Piece'. Also 'End Piece', co-written with Andy Latimer.

16. INVISIBLE MEN (LP)
US Passport PB 6023.
Released December 1983.
Produced by Trevor Vallis and Anthony Phillips.
Recorded at Englewood Studios April – September 1982.
Additional recording and mixing at Atmosphere Studios October – December 1982.
Cover photography by Stephen Marsh.
Side One: 1. Sally (Phillips)/2. Golden Bodies (Phillips/Scott)/3. Going For Broke (Phillips/Scott)/4. Exocet (Phillips/Scott)/5. Love In A Hot Air Balloon (Phillips/Scott)/6. Traces (Phillips/Scott).
Side Two: 7. I Want Your Heart (Phillips/Scott)/8. Falling For Love (Phillips/Scott)/9. Guru (Phillips)/10. The Women Were Watching (Phillips/Scott)/11. My Time Has Come (Phillips).
Anthony Phillips guitars, bass, keyboards, backing vocals. Richard Scott guitars, keyboards, drum machine, backing vocals, vocals. Jeff Dunne, Paul Robinson drums. Morris Pert, Joji Hirota percussion. Bimbo Acock, Martin Drover brass.

CHESTER THOMPSON

1. ROXY AND ELSEWHERE (Frank Zappa and The Mothers)
Discreet UK K69201, US 2202.
Released 1974.

2. ONE SIZE FITS ALL (Frank Zappa and The Mothers)
Discreet UK K59207, US 2216.
Released 1974.

3. BONGO FURY (Frank Zappa and The Mothers)
Discreet UK K59209, US 2234.
Released 1975.

4. YESTERDAY'S DREAM (Alphonso Johnson)
US Epic 34364.
Released 1976.

5. BLACK MARKET (Weather Report)
UK CBS 81325.
US Columbia 34099.
Released 1976.

6. SECONDS OUT (Genesis)
Charisma GE-2001.
Released 1977.

7. PLEASE DON'T TOUCH (Steve Hackett)
Charisma CDS 4012.
Released 1978.

8. A CURIOUS FEELING (Tony Banks)
Charisma CAS 1148.
Released 1979.

9. SLEEP DIRT (Frank Zappa and The Mothers)
Discreet UK K59211, US 2292.
Released 1979.

10. THREE SIDES LIVE (Genesis)
Atlantic SD 2-2000.
Vertigo 6650 008.
Released 1982.

DARYL STUERMER SOLO EFFORTS

1. I LOVE THE BLUES (George Duke)
US BASF BAP 5071.
Released 1975.

2. LIBERATED FANTASIES (George Duke)
US BASF 922835.
Released 1976.

3. IMAGINARY VOYAGE (Jean Luc Ponty)
UK Atlantic K50317.
US Atlantic 18195.
Released 1976.

4. AURORA (Jean Luc Ponty)
UK Atlantic K50228.
Released 1977.

5. ENIGMATIC OCEAN (Jean Luc Ponty)
UK Atlantic K50409.
Released 1977.

6. CIVILISED EVIL (Jean Luc Ponty)
UK Atlantic K50744.

US Atlantic 16020.
Released 1980.

7. FACE VALUE (Phil Collins)
UK Virgin V2185.
US Atlantic SD 16029.
Released 1981.

8. THE SECRET POLICEMAN'S OTHER BALL (Various Artistes)
UK Springtime HAHA 6004.
Released 1982.
Two tracks with Phil Collins.

9. THREE SIDES LIVE (Genesis)
Atlantic SD 2-2000.
Vertigo 6650 008.
Released 1982.

10. ACTING VERY STRANGE (Mike Rutherford)
WEA K99249.
Released 1982.

11. HELLO, I MUST BE GOING! (Phil Collins)
Virgin V2252.
Released 1982.

12. THE FUGITIVE (Tony Banks)
Charisma TBLP 1.
Released 1983.

SOLO EFFORTS

The Lamb Lies Down on Broadway CGS 101

Available on Charisma Records

COMPILATIONS

1. WOWIE ZOWIE – THE WORLD OF PROGRESSIVE MUSIC
Decca SPA 34.
Released 1969.
Includes 'In The Beginning' from Genesis.

2. ONE MORE CHANCE
Charisma CLASS 3.
Released 1973.
Compilation of Charisma singles on album. Includes Genesis non-album track 'Happy The Man'.

3. THE STORY OF POP
K-Tel TE 295/6.
Released 1973.
Includes edited version of 'The Knife' from Genesis.

4. THE FAMOUS CHARISMA LABEL – VOLUME ONE
Fontana 9286 867 – Italy only.
Released 1973.
Includes 'Happy The Man', 'Twilight Alehouse', and single version of 'Watcher Of The Skies' from Genesis.

5. CHARISMA DISTURBANCE
Charisma TSS 1.
Released 1973.
Double album to celebrate first four years of Charisma Records. Includes 'The Return Of The Giant Hogweed' from Genesis.

6. CHARISMA FESTIVAL
Charisma 6369 930 – Italy only.
Released 1973.
Includes 'Time Table' and single version of 'Watcher Of The Skies'.

7. CHARISMA KEYBOARDS
Charisma CLASS 5.
Released 1974.
Sampler of Charisma's keyboard-based bands. Includes 'Fountain Of Salmacis' from Genesis. Through a mix-up this catalogue number was later also used for the Brand X album 'Livestock'.

8. MUSIC EXPLOSION
K-Tel TE 305.
Released 1974.
Includes edited version of 'I Know What I Like' from Genesis.

9. THE OLD GREY WHISTLE TEST – TAKE TWO
BBC Records BEDP 001.
Released 1976.
Includes 'Ripples' from Genesis.

10. SUPERTRACKS
Vertigo SPORT 1.
Released 1977.
Compiled by Tony Stratton-Smith in aid of the Sports Foundation. Includes 'Carpet Crawl' from Genesis.

11. LONDON ARTISTS COLLECTOR SERIES
London Records Canada LC-X-1004.
Released 1977.
Includes 'The Conqueror' from Genesis.

12. PROFILES IN GOLD – ALBUM 2
Warner Special Products OP-7502.
Released 1978.
7" 33⅓rpm EP includes 'Follow You Follow Me' and 'Your Own Special Way' from Genesis.

13. HITWAVE
Polystar Australia 9199-959.
Released 1978.
Includes 'Follow You Follow Me' from Genesis.

14. AN EXCLUSIVE GIFT FROM DECCA
Decca SFI-1471.
Released 1979.
Promo flexidisc with gold finish, includes 'Silent Sun' from Genesis.

15. AN HOUR OF POP HITS – REELS ON WHEELS
Mercury REEL 002.
Released 1979.
Cassette-only compilation including 'Solsbury Hill' from Peter Gabriel.

16. AN HOUR OF ROCK VOL.2 – REELS ON WHEELS
Mercury REEL 004.
Released 1979.
Cassette-only compilation including 'Modern Love' from Peter Gabriel.

17. THE HITMAKERS
Polystar HOP TV 1.
Released 1980.
Includes Genesis 'Turn It On Again', Peter Gabriel 'Games Without Frontiers'.

18. LOST AND FOUND
Decca DPA 3083/4
Released 1980.
Includes 'Silent Sun' and 'In The Wilderness" from Genesis.

19. SOUNDS/CHARISMA MASTERPIECES
Sounds/Charisma SS6.
Released 1980.
Includes Genesis 'Match Of The Day', Mike Rutherford 'Moonshine' (remixed), Steve Hackett 'Tigermoth' (live).

20. THE OLD GREY WHISTLE TEST – TEST PRESSING
BBC Records BELP 017.
Released 1980.
Includes Genesis 'Please Don't Ask'.

21. REPEAT PERFORMANCE
Charisma BG 1.
Released 1980.
Includes Genesis 'I Know What I Like',
Peter Gabriel 'Solsbury Hill', Steve
Hackett 'Every Day'.

22. RADIO ACTIVE
Ronco RTL 2019.
Released 1980.
Includes Genesis 'Misunderstanding'.

23. HOT WAX
K-Tel NE 1082.
Released 1980.
Includes Genesis 'Turn It On Again',
Peter Gabriel 'No Self Control'.

24. MONSTER TRACKS
Polystar HOPTV 2.
Released 1981.
Includes Genesis 'Abacab'.

25. SPACE INVASION
Ronco RTL 2051.
Released 1981.
Includes Genesis 'Watcher Of The Skies'.

26. BEST OF TOP OF THE POPS VOL.9
BBC Records BELP 018.
Released 1981.
Includes Phil Collins 'In The Air Tonight'.

27. LIFE IN THE EUROPEAN THEATRE
WEA K58412.
Released 1981.
Anti-nuclear benefit album, includes
Peter Gabriel 'I Don't Remember'.

28. THE MARQUEE COLLECTION VOLUME 1 – 1958-1983 (Various artistes)
UK England Records MAR 1.
Released June 1983.
Includes 'I Know What I Like (In Your
Wardrobe) (Live)' from Genesis.

29. THE MARQUEE COLLECTION VOLUME 3 – 1958-1983 (Various artistes)

UK England Records MAR 3.
Released June 1983.
Includes 'Turn It On Again (Live)' from Genesis.

30. NOW THAT'S WHAT I CALL MUSIC (Various artistes)

UK EMI/Virgin NOW 1.
Released December 1983.
Includes Phil Collins 'You Can't Hurry Love' and Genesis 'That's All'.

COMPILATIONS

GENESIS
A Trick of the Tail
CDS 4001
New Album on Charisma Records

'solid gold success'
Barbara Charone, Sounds, Feb. 7th

'sheer excellence'
Chris Welch, Melody Maker, Feb. 7th

'quite remarkable'
Steve Clarke, NME, Feb. 14th

'a very sophisticated piece of work'
Angus MacKinnon, Streetlife, Feb. 21st

COVERS

1. YOU'LL NEVER KNOW/I'M BIG ENOUGH FOR ME (Charlie Drake)
UK Charisma single CB270.
Released 1975.
Written by Peter Gabriel/Martin Hall.
Produced by Peter Gabriel.

2. BULLY FOR YOU (Robinson/ Gabriel)/OUR PEOPLE (Robinson) (Tom Robinson Band)
UK EMI EMI 2916.
Released 1976.
A-side which was co-written by Gabriel, and which he has performed live, was not officially released on record.

5. BEHIND THE LINES (Banks/ Collins/Rutherford) (Phil Collins)
UK album track on 'Face Value' Virgin V2185.
Released 1981.
Although co-written by Collins, the first real cover version of any Genesis track.

3. GET THE GUNS/MYSTIFIED (artiste not known)
UK Good Earth single GD 14.
Released 1977.
A-side written by Peter Gabriel and Martin Hall.

4. ANIMALS HAVE MORE FUN (Pursey/Gabriel/Ellis)/SUS (Pursey/ Gabriel/Ellis) (Jimmy Pursey)
UK Epic EPC-A 1336.
Released 1981.
Also produced by Peter Gabriel.

**6. THIS MUST BE LOVE (Collins)/
YOU'LL NEVER KNOW WHAT
YOU'RE MISSING (C.Amoo/E.Amoo)
(Chris Amoo)**
UK Precision PAR 118.
Released 1981.
Vocalist from 'The Real Thing'.

**7. IF LEAVING ME IS EASY
(Collins)/GIVE ME A LITTE MORE
(Charmers) (Lloyd Charmers)**
UK Radioactive RAD 3 (12).
Released 1982.
Extended 12" single reggae version.

**8. NORTH BY NORTHWEST
(Tom Robinson)**
UK Panic ROBBO 1.
Released June, 1982.
Includes two songs written by Robinson/
Gabriel: 'Atmospherics' and 'Merrily On
High'.

9. SOMETHING'S GOING ON (Frida)
UK Epic EPC 85966.
Released September, 1982.
Includes 'You Know What I Mean' written
by Phil Collins.

PRODUCTION WORK

**1. ANIMALS HAVE MORE FUN
(Pursey/Gabriel/Ellis)/SUS (Pursey/
Gabriel/Ellis) (Jimmy Pursey)**
UK Epic EPC-A 1336.
Released 1981.
Produced by Peter Gabriel.

2. GLORIOUS FOOL (John Martyn)
UK WEA K99178.
US Duke DU 19345.
Released 1981.
Produced by Phil Collins.
Duke Records is Genesis' own label.

**3. PLEASE FALL IN LOVE WITH ME
(Martyn)/DON'T YOU GO (Martyn)
(John Martyn)**
UK WEA K79243.
Released 1981.
Taken from 'Glorious Fool' album.
Produced by Phil Collins.

**4. I KNOW THERE'S SOMETHING
GOING ON (Ballard)/THRENODY
(Parker/Gessle) (Frida)**
UK Epic EPC-A 2603.
Released August 1982.
Produced by Phil Collins.

5. SOMETHING'S GOING ON (Frida)
UK Epic EPC 85966.
Released 1982.
Produced by Phil Collins.

**6. PUSS IN BOOTS (Ant/Marco)/
KISS THE DRUMMER (Ant/Marco)
(ADAM ANT)**
CBS A 3614 (Single).
CBS WA 3614 (picture disc).
Released October 1983.
A-side produced by Phil Collins.

7. STRIP (Adam Ant)
CBS CBS 25705 (Album).
Released November 1983.
Two tracks produced by Phil Collins –
'Puss In Boots' and 'Strip'.

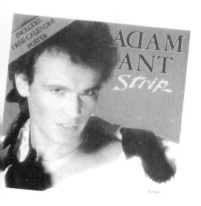

**8. STRIP (Ant/Marco)/YOURS,
YOURS, YOURS (Ant/Marco)
(ADAM ANT)**
CBS A 3589 (Single).
Released January 1984.
A-side produced by Phil Collins.

BOOTLEGS

GENESIS ALBUMS

1. LIVE AT THE MARQUEE CLUB 1972
TAKRL 932, good mono, poor at times.
Side One: 1. Watcher Of The Skies/
2. Can Utility And The Coastliners/
3. The Musical Box.
Side Two: 4. Return Of The Giant
Hogweed/5. The Knife.

2. LIVE IN NEWCASTLE 26 OCTOBER 1973
TAKRL 24905, good stereo.
Side One: 1. Watcher Of The Skies/
2. Dancing Lotta The Moonlit Knight(!)
Side Two: 3. Cinema Show/4. I Know
What I Likes/5. Firth Of Fifth.

3. QUEBEC CITY 3 MARCH 1973
Wombat Records, 55 min., good stereo.
Side One: 1. Get 'Em Out By Friday/
2. Musical Box/3. Return Of The Giant
Hogweed.
Side Two: 4. Supper's Ready.

4. A DEATH IN ANYTOWN 22 NOVEMBER 1973
TAKRL 24906, 115 min., very good stereo.
Recorded at Los Angeles Forum.
Side One: 1. Watcher Of The Skies/
2. Firth Of Fifth/3. Musical Box.
Side Two: 4. Dancing With The
Moonlit Knight/5. Cinema Show/6. I
Know What I Like.
Side Three: 7. Supper's Ready.
Side Four: 8. Horizons/9. More Fool
Me/10. Battle Of Epping Forest/11. The
Knife.

5. CARNEGIE HALL 1973
TAKRL 933, 60 min., very good mono.
Side One: 1. Watcher Of The Skies/
2. Musical Box.
Side Two: 3. Get 'Em Out By Friday/
4. Supper's Ready.

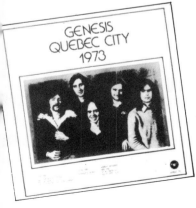

6. THE BEDSIDE YELLOW FOAM 1974
TAKRL 1955, 50 min., very good mono.
Side One: 1. Dancing With The
Moonlit Knight/2. Cinema Show/Aisle
Of Plenty (UK Jan. 1974).
Side Two: 3. Supper's Ready (Canada
November, 1974).

BOOTLEGS

7. L'ANGE GABRIEL 21 APRIL 1974
Smilin' Ears 7705, 55 min., excellent stereo.
Recorded at Montreal University.
　　Side One: 1. Dancing With The Moonlit Knight/2. Cinema Show.
　　Side Two: 3. I Know What I Like/ 4. Firth Of Fifth/5. Musical Box.

9. REVELATION WITHOUT A CAUSE MARCH 1975
Wizardo WRMB 313, 45 min., good stereo.
Recorded at Shrine Auditorium, Los Angeles.
　　Side One: 1. Silent Sorrow/2. Colony Of Slippermen/3. Ravine/4. The Light Dies Down On Broadway/5. Riding The Scree.
　　Side Two: 6. The Waiting Room/ 7. Anyway/8. The Supernatural Anaesthetist/9. The Lamia.

10. AWED MAN OUT 15 APRIL 1975
TAKRL 1975, 55 min., excellent stereo.
　　Side One: 1. Cuckoo Cocoon/2. Back In NYC/3. Hairless Heart/4. Carpet Crawl/5. Lilywhite Lilith.
　　Side Two: 6. Waiting Room/ 7. Anyway/8. Ravine/9. The Light Dies Down On Broadway/10. Riding The Scree.

8. AS THOUGH EMERALD CITY MARCH 1975
TAKRL 1945, 50 min., excellent stereo.
Recorded Shrine Auditorium, Los Angeles.
　　Side One: 1. Watcher Of The Skies/ 2. Lilywhite Lilith/3. The Waiting Room/ 4. Anyway/5. It
　　Side Two: 6. Musical Box/7. Happy The Man/8. Twilight Alehouse.
　　Last two tracks are studio.

11. SWELLED AND SPENT
2 MAY 1975
TAKRL 2980, 105 min., good stereo.
Recorded at Birmingham, UK.
Side One: 1. The Lamb Lies Down On Broadway/2. Fly On A Windshield/ 3. Broadway Melody Of 1974/4. Cuckoo Cocoon/5. In The Cage/6. The Grand Parade.
Side Two: 7. Back In NYC/8. Hairless Heart/9. Counting Out Time/10. Carpet Crawl/11. Chamber Of 32 Doors.
Side Three: 12. Lilywhite Lilith/ 13. Waiting Room/14. Anyway/ 15. Supernatural Anaesthetist/16. The Lamia.
Side Four: 17. Colony Of Slippermen/ 18. Ravine/19. The Light Dies Down On Broadway/20. Riding The Scree/21. In The Rapids/22. It.

12. TWO DOWN THREE LEFT
14 APRIL 1976
Dancin' Disc Records 1001, 50 min., very good stereo.
Recorded at Cleveland, U.S.A.
Side One: 1. The Lamb Lies Down On Broadway/2. Fly On A Windshield/ 3. Carpet Crawl/4. Cinema Show.
Side Two: 5. Robbery Assault & Battery/6. I Know What I Like/7. Los Endos/8. It/9. Watcher Of The Skies.

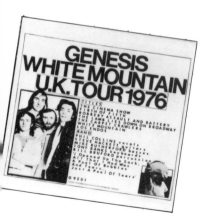

13. WHITE MOUNTAIN
UK TOUR 1976
G.9201, 50 min., excellent stereo.
Side One: 1. Cinema Show/2. Firth Of Fifth/3. Robbery Assault & Battery.
Side Two: 4. The Lamb Lies Down On Broadway/5. Fly On A Windshield/ 6. Carpet Crawl/7. White Mountain/ 8. Los Endos.

14. LIVE AT THE RAINBOW
2 JANUARY 1977
Sweede S-001, 45 min, very good stereo.
Side One: 1. In That Quiet Earth/ 2. Afterglow/3. Firth Of Fifth/4. All In A Mouse's Night.
Side Two: 5. One For The Vine/6. The Lamb Lies Down On Broadway/ 7. Musical Box.

15. A LIVING STORY JANUARY 1977
Big Thumb PG1300, 40 min., excellent stereo.
Side One: 1. Squonk/2. Afterglow (track is actually 'All In A Mouse's Night'/ 3. Eleventh Earl Of Mar.
Side Two: 4. One For The Vine/5. I Know What I Like.

16. ALL WE NEED'S A HIT
Catalogue number 1597, 65 min., fair mono.
Recorded at Earls Court, London 23rd June 1977, 24th June 1977 and Manchester 11th January 1977.
Side One: 1. Squonk/2. One For The Vine/3. Your Own Special Way/4. Inside And Out.
Side Two: 5. Carpet Crawl/6. Afterglow/ 7. Eleventh Earl Of Mar/8. I Know What I Like/9. Dance On A Volcano/10. The Lamb Lies Down On Broadway/ 11. Musical Box.

17. LIVING REVELATIONS, EARLS
COURT 24 JUNE 1977
KMH 2077, 50 min., excellent stereo.
Side One: 1. One For The Vine/ 2. Inside And Out/3. Firth Of Fifth.
Side Two: 4. Dance On A Volcano/ 5. Los Endos/6. The Lamb Lies Down On Broadway/7. Musical Box/8. The Knife.

18. LIVE IN GERMANY MAY 1978
Novisad ST-C56873, 40 min.
Incorrect track listing on cover.
Side One: 1. One For The Vine Part II/
2. In The Cage/3. Deep In The
Motherlode.
Side Two: 4. Follow You Follow Me/
5. Burning Rope/6. Ballad Of Big.

**19. AND THEN THERE WAS
GABRIEL 29 JULY 1978**
TKE 8779, excellent stereo.
Side One: 1. Burning Rope/
2. Fountain Of Salmacis/3. Ballad Of Big.
Side Two: 4. Say It's Alright Joe/
5. Follow You Follow Me/6.* I Know What
I Like.

*Features Collins and Gabriel on
vocals, hence title.

20. SOME OLD, SOME NEW
Triple boxed set, very good stereo.
Side One: 1. Get 'Em Out By Friday/
2. Twilight Alehouse/3. Watcher Of The
Skies (John Peel Session 1972).

Side Two: 4. Supper's Ready (Toronto
1977).
Side Three: 5. Squonk/6. One For The
Vine/7. Robbery Assault & Battery
(Toronto 1977).
Side Four: 8. Your Own Special Way/
9. Firth Of Fifth/10. Carpet Crawl (Toronto
1977).
Side Five: 11. In That Quiet Earth/
12. Afterglow/13. I Know What I Like
(Toronto 1977).
Side Six: 14. On The Air/15. White
Shadow/16. Solsbury Hill/17. Here
Comes The Flood/18. The Lamb Lies
Down On Broadway (Peter Gabriel –
KBFH Broadcast of Bottom Line 4th
October 1978).

**21. FROM THE MOUTH OF THE
MONSTER 13 OCTOBER 1978**
Atlantis GTT 78, 95 min., excellent stereo.
Recorded at Uptown Theatre, Chicago.
Side One: 1. Burning Rope/
2. Dancing With The Moonlit Knight (full
version)/3. Musical Box (closing section)/
4. Say It's Alright Joe.
Side Two: 5. Deep In The Motherlode/
6. Ripples/7. The Lady Lies.
Side Three: 8. Cinema Show/9. In That
Quiet Earth/10. Afterglow.
Side Four: 11. Follow You Follow Me/
12. Dance On A Volcano/13. Los Endos/
14. In The Cage.

**22. LIVING IN A TWILIGHT
ALEHOUSE 28 JUNE 1972**
TKE 11780, 300 numbered copies, good
mono.
Recorded at Watford Town Hall.
Side One: 1. Stagnation/2. Fountain Of
Salmacis/3. Peter Gabriel Talks (Montreal
Radio 21st April 1974).
Side Two: 4. Happy The Man/
5. Twilight Alehouse/6. Musical Box.

**23. RECORDED LIVE AT THE FELT
FORUM 1973**
TAKRL 24906, New York, very good
stereo.
Side One: 1. Watcher Of The Skies/
2. Can Utility And The Coastliners/
3. Musical Box.
Side Two: 4. Dancing With The
Moonlit Knight/5. The Cinema Show/6. I
Know What I Like (In Your Wardrobe).
Side Three: 7. Supper's Ready.
Side Four: 8. Instrumental/9. More
Fool Me/10. The Battle Of Epping
Forest/11. The Knife.

**24. YOU'LL LOVE US LIVE
7 MAY 1980**
Rainbow GFLE 002, excellent stereo.
Side One: 1. Turn It On Again Part II/
2. Follow You Follow Me/3. I Know What
I Like/4. The Knife/5. In The Cage Part II/
6. Raven/7. Afterglow Part I.

Side Two: 8. Carpet Crawl/9. Squonk/
10. Behind The Lines/11. Duchess, Guide
Vocal.

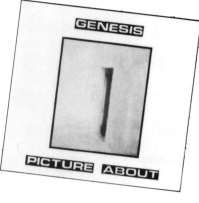

25. REVELATORY GENESIS 80:78
Steam 80001, excellent stereo.
From Lyceum 7th May, 1980 and
Knebworth 24th June, 1980.
  Side One: 1. Deep In The Motherlode/
2. One For The Vine/3. The Lady Lies.
  Side Two: 4. Follow You Follow Me/
5. Behind The Lines/6. Duchess/7. Guide
Vocal/8. Turn It On Again.
  Side Three: 9. Duke's Travels/
10. Duke's End/11. Dance On A
Volcano/12. Los Endos.
  Side Four: 13. Burning Rope/
14. Fountain Of Salmacis/15. The Knife.

27. PICTURE ABOUT – FREJUS, FRANCE 27 SEPTEMBER 1981
Original Records MCR 71GE 81/10,
three-record boxed set.
  Side One: 1. Behind The Lines/
2. Duchess/3. The Lamb Lies Down On
Broadway.
  Side Two: 4. Dodo/5. Abacab.
  Side Three: 6. Misunderstanding/
7. Firth Of Fifth.
  Side Four: 8. Me And Ser Yack(!)/
9. In The Cage.
  Side Five: 10. Turn It On Again/
11. Dance On A Vulcano.
  Side Six: 12. Los Endos/13. I Know
What I Like.

26. THE RAREST (LIVE)
Stemra SABAM 5001.
  Side One: 1. Stagnation/2. Get 'Em
Out By Friday/3. Twilight Alehouse (BBC
Sessions).
  Side Two: 4. Moonlit Knight/
5. Horizons/6. Battle Of Epping Forest
(Montreal 21st April 1974).

28. PERILOUS SCHIZOPHRENIA – NUERNBERG 9 OCTOBER 1981
Laughing Spoon LSR 001, limited to 500
copies.
  Side One: Applause/1. Behind The
Lines/2. Dutches(!)/Applause/3. The
Lamb Lies Down On Broadway/
Applause/Phil speaks German/4. Dodo.
  Side Two: 5. Abacab/Applause/Phil

speaks German/6. Man On The Corner/
7. Who Dunnit/Applause/Phil speaks/
8. Carpet Crawlers/Applause.

29. GENESIS IN CONCERT – DRURY LANE 4 MAY 1980
Gold Records WARSTR 3-C.
Side One: 1. Dancing In The Moonlit Knight/2. Carpet Crawlers/3. Squonk/
4. Behind The Lines.
Side Two: 5. Duchess/Guide Vocal/
6. Turn It On Again/7. Ripples.
Side Three: 8. In The Cage/9. Raven/
10. Afterglow/11. Follow You Follow Me/
12. Carpet Crawlers.
Side Four: 13. I Know What I Like/
14. The Knife/15. Back In NYC.
'Carpet Crawlers' and 'Back In NYC' from 'Awed Man Out'.

30. ODDITIES IN THE CAGE VOLUME 1
PG 2681.
Side One: 1. The Angel Gabriel (sung by Kate Bush and Steve Harley, German TV '79)/2. Just Another Day (PG and Kate Bush duet, German TV '79)/3. Why Don't We (PG, Cleveland Music Hall, 15th July 1977, included sections that became 'Family Snapshot')/4. Ich Und Mein Teddy Bear/5. Happy Birthday/6. Teddy Bear (French)/7. A Whiter Shade Of Pale (punk version)/8. Let It Be (PG, Kate Bush, Steve Harley).
Side Two: 9. Silver Song (unreleased Genesis song featuring PC, AP and MR, BBC Radio '74)/10. Inside And Out/
11. Girl In The Green Trouser Suit (a PG on stage story '73)/12. Harold The Barrel/
13. Evil Jam.
Side One Gabriel, Side Two Genesis.

31. FLAMING MOUTH (Single)
7" 33⅓rpm (picture sleeve).
Side One: 1. Evil Jam (live 1975).
Side Two: Fountain Of Salmacis (live 1978).

PETER GABRIEL ALBUMS

1. PETER GABRIEL AT THE ROXY, LOS ANGELES 9 APRIL 1977 (Double)
PG1200, excellent stereo.
Side One: 1. Here Comes The Flood/
2. Moribund The Burgermeister/
3. Waiting For The Big One/4. A Song Without Words.
Side Two: 5. Excuse Me/6. Solsbury Hill/7. Ain't That Peculiar/8. Humdrum.
Side Three: 9. Slowburn/10. All Day And All Of The Night/11. Here Comes The Flood.
Side Four: 12. Modern Love/13. Down The Dolce Vita/14. Back In NYC.

2. PETER GABERIAL (SIC) – GILDED SLEEVE ROXY, LOS ANGELES 9 APRIL 1977.
FLAT 8234, excellent stereo.
Side One: 1. Here Comes The Flood/
2. Maribond(!)/3. The Burgermeister/
4. Waiting For The Big One/5. A Song Without Words.
Side Two: 6. Excuse Me/7. Solsbury Hill/8. Ain't That Peculiar/9. Humdrum/
10. Slowburn/11. All Day And All Of The Night.

3. THE EGG WAS A BIRD – COPENHAGEN 9 OCTOBER 1977
How To Walk Silly Records HTWSR 101, very good stereo, Swedish.
100 numbered copies red vinyl and poster.
100 unnumbered copies black vinyl no poster.
Side One: 1. Moribund The Burgermeister/2. Indigo/3. Humdrum/
4. White Shadow/5. Down The Dolce Vita.
Side Two: 6. I Heard It Through The Grapevine/7. On The Air/8. All Day And All Of The Night/9. Strawberry Fields Forever (last is studio with LSO).

4. LIKE A POSSESSED 12-YEAR OLD-NEW VICTORIA, LONDON 30 APRIL 1977

JAP, good mono.

Side One: 1. Here Comes The Flood/
2. Moribund The Burgermeister/
3. Waiting For The Big One/4. Mickey Mouse/5. Excuse Me/6. Ain't That Peculiar/7. Solsbury Hill.

Side Two: 8. Slowburn/9. All Day And All Of The Night/10. Modern Love/
11. Down The Dolce Vita/12. Back In NYC.

5. SUBMERGE – 1977/78

Impossible Recordworks IMP 2-22, excellent stereo.

Recorded at Roxy, Los Angeles 1977, (Sides 1 - 3).

Recorded at Bottom Line, New York 1978. (Side 4).

Side One: 1. Here Comes The Flood/
2. Moribund The Burgermeister/
3. Mickey Mouse/4. Excuse Me/
5. Solsbury Hill.

Side Two: 6. Ain't That Peculiar/
7. Humdrum, Slowburn/8. All Day And All Of The Night.

Side Three: 9. Modern Love/10. Down The Dolce Vita/11. Back In NYC.

Side Four: 12. On The Air/13. White Shadow/14. D.I.Y./15. Here Comes The Flood II/16. The Lamb Lies Down On Broadway.

6. RAEL FEBRUARY 1978

Blue Line BLR 21.

Listed as recorded at Paris Olympia, but possibly incorrect.

Side One: 1. Heard It Through The Grapevine/2. Solsbury Hill/3. Animal Magic.

Side Two: 4. Down The Dolce Vita/
5. Modern Love/6. Indigo.

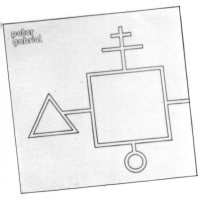

7. LIVE IN GENEVA 17 DECEMBER 1978

(98), Euro bootleg silver/blue cover, good mono.

Side One: 1. New Song/2. White Shadow/3. D.I.Y./4. Waiting For The Big One.

Side Two: 5. Slowburn/6. Solsbury Hill/7. Modern Love.

8. I LOST MY TEDDY BEAR ON THE 1980 TOUR

AVP 107, 200 numbered copies, OK mono.

Recorded at Cleveland Music Hall, 27th June 1980.

Side One: 1. Solsbury Hill/2. Family Snapshot/3. Milgram's 37/4. Modern Love/5. Lead A Normal Life.

Side Two: 6. Mother Of Violence/
7. Humdrum/8. Games Without Frontiers/9. I Go Swiming/10. Here Comes The Flood.

9. PETER GABRIEL: THE NEW TWO INEDIT TRACES

(The two new unreleased tracks) Italian single (picture sleeve).

No catalogue number.

Side One: Miligrans 37 (Gabriel) Turin 30th September 1980 (should be Milgram's 37).

Side Two: I Go Swimming (Gabriel) Genoa 29th September, 1980.

10. FRONT TEAR GAMES

Recorded at Hammersmith Odeon London, 12th March 1980, Maple Leaf Gardens 3rd July 1980, Stoney Brook NYC 24th October 1980, Leicester 24th February 1980, Chicago '79, Diplomat Hotel, NYC, July 1980.

Side One: 1. Intruder/2. Start/3. I Don't Remember/4. Family Snapshots/5. Lead A Normal Life.

Side Two: 6. Milgram's 37/7. Mother Of Violence/8. Games Without Frontiers/9. I Go Swimming.

Side Three: 10. Bully For You/11. And Through The Wire/12. Not One Of Us/13. Biko.

Side Four: 14. On The Air/
15. Moribund The Burgermeister/
16. White Shadow/17. Ain't That Peculiar/18. Humdrum.

11. ON STAGE, ITALY SEPTEMBER 1980

Side One: 1. Intruder/2. Start/3. I Don't Remember/4. Solsbury Hill.

Side Two: 5. Mother Of Violence/
6. Games Without Frontiers/7. And Through The Wire/8. I Go Swimming/
9. On The Air/10. Here Comes The Flood.

D U K E
....IT WAS WELL WORTH THE WAIT

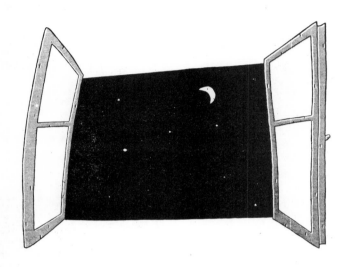

G E N E S I S

ALBUM: CBR 101 TAPE: CBRC 101

INCLUDES THE SINGLE "TURN IT ON AGAIN" CB 356
PRODUCED BY DAVID HENTSCHEL AND GENESIS

TAPES

COMMERCIAL

1. ROCK ROOTS
Decca KRTC 1.

2. TRESPASS
Charisma ZCCAS 1020.
Charisma 7208 551.

3. NURSERY CRYME
Charisma ZCCAS 1052.
Charisma 7208 552.

4. FOXTROT
Charisma ZCCAS 1058.
Charisma 7208 553.

5. GENESIS LIVE
Charisma 7299 288.

6. SELLING ENGLAND BY THE POUND
Charisma ZCCAS 1074.
Charisma 7208 554.

7. THE LAMB LIES DOWN ON BROADWAY
Charisma 7599 121.

8. A TRICK OF THE TAIL
Charisma 7208 602.

9. WIND AND WUTHERING
Charisma 7208 611.

10. SECONDS OUT
Charisma 7649 067

11. ... AND THEN THERE WERE THREE ...
Charisma 7208 619.

12. DUKE
Charisma CBRC 101.

13. ABACAB
Charisma CBRC 102.
Vertigo 7144 162.

14. THREE SIDES LIVE
Charisma GEC 2002.
Atlantic TP 2-2000.

15. GENESIS
Charisma/Virgin GENMC 1.

SOLO RELEASES

1. A CURIOUS FEELING (Tony Banks)
Charisma 7208 627.

2. THE FUGITIVE (Tony Banks)
Charisma TBMC 1.

3. FACE VALUE (Phil Collins)
Virgin TCV 2185.

4. HELLO, I MUST BE GOING! (Phil Collins)
Virgin TCV 2252.

5. SMALLCREEP'S DAY (Mike Rutherford)
Charisma 7208 628.

**6. ACTING VERY STRANGE
(Mike Rutherford)**
WEA K499249.

7. PETER GABRIEL I
Charisma 7208 612.

8. PETER GABRIEL II
Charisma 7208 621.

9. PETER GABRIEL III
Charisma 7150 015.

10. PETER GABRIEL IV
Charisma PGMC 4.

11. PETER GABRIEL PLAYS LIVE
Charisma PGDMC1.

**12. VOYAGE OF THE ACOLYTE
(Steve Hackett)**
Charisma 7208 555.

**13. SPECTRAL MORNINGS
(Steve Hackett)**
Chrysalis CCH 1223.

**14. VOYAGE OF THE ACOLYTE/
PLEASE DON'T TOUCH (Steve
Hackett)**
Charisma Double Play CHMC 105.

15. DEFECTOR (Steve Hackett)
Charisma 7208 630.
Charisma CHCMC 15.

16. CURED (Steve Hackett)
Charisma 7144 153.

17. HIGHLY STRUNG (Steve Hackett)
Charisma HAKMC 1.

18. BAY OF KINGS (Steve Hackett)
Lamborghini ZCLMG 3000.

**19. THE GEESE AND THE GHOST
(Anthony Phillips)**
Hit & Run Music ZCHIT 001.
PVC PVCC 8905.

**20. PRIVATE PARTS & PIECES II
(Anthony Phillips)**
PVC PVCC 7913.

21. SIDES (Anthony Phillips)
Passport PBC 9834.

22. 1984 (Anthony Phillips)
RCA K5036.
Passport PBC 6006.

**23. PRIVATE PARTS & PIECES III –
ANTIQUES (Anthony Phillips)**
RCA INTK 5228.

NON COMMERCIAL

1. SOUNDS OF THE SEVENTIES
BBC May 1971.
'Musical Box', 'Stagnation'.

2. MARQUEE
10 min. 1971.

**3. IN CONCERT also titled
BRITISH TV**
25 min.

4. WATFORD TECHNICAL COLLEGE
22 November, 1971. 65 min.

5. GENESIS UK TOURS 1971/2/3
1971 BBC in Concert. 1972 BBC
Sessions. 1973 Bob Harris Radio Show.

6. WATFORD TOWN HALL
28 June, 1972. 80 min.

7. VIAREGGIO, ITALY
20 August, 1972. 50 min.

8. GENOA, ITALY
22 August, 1972.

9. ORTF PARIS
August 1972. 35 min.

10. DUBLIN
28 September, 1972. 45 min.

11. JOHN PEEL SESSION
September 1972.

12. SHARPENED TO THE HILT
. Live from BBC Radio Sessions 1972.

13. CANADIAN TV
1972. 45 min.

14. PARIS
September 1973. 90 min.

15. LAUSANNE
September 1973. 90 min.

16. THE RAINBOW, LONDON
20 October, 1973. 105 min.
Taken from the USA transmission of the
Capital Radio (London) broadcast.

17. BRITISH TV
October 1973. 60 min.

18. MOONSWEPT PARADISE
1973.

**19. SELLING LIVE SONGS BY THE
POUND**
Bristol 1973.

20. THANKSGIVING
Felt Forum, Los Angeles – Thanksgiving
Day 25 November, 1973.

21. ROXY L.A.
17 December, 1973. 90 min.

22. BRISTOL
1974. 50 min.

23. CANADIAN RADIO BROADCAST
21 April, 1974. 105 min.
Montreal University Sports Center.
Same broadcast used for 'L'Ange
Gabriel' LP.

24. PROVIDENCE, R.I.
8 December, 1974.

25. WATERBURY, CONNECTICUT
12 December, 1974.

26. STUTTGART, GERMANY
2 April, 1975. 105 min.

27. EMPIRE POOL, WEMBLEY
15 April, 1975. 45 min.

28. KBFH (WEMBLEY)
15 April, 1975. 30 min.

29. SWEDISH RADIO BROADCAST
Empire Pool, Wembley 15 April, 1975.
30 min.

30. BROTHER JOHN IS NO.9
Empire Pool, Wembley 15 April, 1975.
Entire 'Lamb' set plus 'Musical Box'.

31. MANCHESTER
27 April, 1975. 110 min.

32. FAREWELL BRITANNIA
Birmingham Hippodrome 2 May, 1975.
Entire 'Lamb' set plus 'Musical Box' and
'The Knife'.

33. REIMS DE PARIS
15 May, 1975.
(Gabriel's last ever gig with Genesis).

34. PITTSBURGH
13 April, 1976. 100 min.
Taken from WDVE FM radio broadcast.

35. CLEVELAND
15 April, 1976. 100 min.

36. STAFFORD
1976. 45 min.

37. IN CONCERT
1976. Soundtrack from the film. 45 min.

38. STARLIGHT BOWL
1 May, 1976.

39. HAMMERSMITH ODEON
June 1976. 115 min.

40. GOTHENBURG, SWEDEN
30 June, 1976. 120 min.

41. GLASGOW APOLLO
9 July, 1976. 110 min.

42. BISCUIT KING TEA TIME
UK Tour 1976.
From US radio broadcast.

43. ROMEO AND JULIET
World Tour 1977. Stereo.

44. RAINBOW LONDON
1 January, 1977. 120 min.

**45. MANCHESTER FREE TRADE
HALL**
11 January, 1977. 120 min.

46. BRISTOL HIPPODROME
1977.

47. EDINBURGH
15 January, 1977. 90 min.

48. LEICESTER
21 January, 1977. 90 min.

49. CHICAGO
6 February, 1977. 130 min.

50. STOCKHOLM
4 June, 1977. 125 min.

51. EARLS COURT
24 June, 1977. 120 min.
From Capital Radio (with ads).

52. EARLS COURT
24 June, 1977. 120 min.
Repeat of Capital broadcast but with
different track order.

53. PENN STATE UNIVERSITY
2 April, 1978. 90 min.

54. KALAMAZOO, MICHIGAN
4 April, 1978. 120 min.

55. MALMO, SWEDEN
6 June, 1978. 130 min.

56. GOTHENBURG, SWEDEN
7 June, 1978. 140 min.

**57. A MIDSUMMER NIGHT'S
DREAM**
24 June, 1978. 90 min.
Knebworth, Herts. Several versions exist
mostly from BBC radio broadcast.

58. ON THE ROAD
1978. 50 min.
Soundtrack from BBC TV 'Nationwide'
documentary.

59. MONTREAL
13 July, 1978.

60. MADISON SQUARE GARDEN
29 July, 1978. New York. 145 min.

**61. BEST LIVE BAND IN THE
WORLD**
Stereo from 1976/77/78.

62. ROTTERDAM, HOLLAND
6 September, 1978.

63. FRIAR'S AYLESBURY
23 March, 1980.

64. HAPPY BIRTHDAY TONY
27 March, 1980. London Hammersmith
Odeon. Whole set minus 'The Knife'.

65. TISWAS BLUES
28 March, 1980. London Hammersmith
Odeon.

66. HAMMERSMITH ODEON
29 March, 1980. Whole set.

67. FOR THE LOVE OF ALBERT
3 April, 1980. Peterborough. Whole set
minus 'The Knife'.

68. CARDIFF
9 April, 1980. Whole set.

69. SHEFFIELD
17 April, 1980. 150 min.
Radio Hallam broadcast, whole set with
stories.

70. EDINBURGH
23 April, 1980. Whole set.

71. GLASGOW
27 April, 1980. Whole set.

72. GLASGOW
28 April, 1980. Whole set.

73. LIVERPOOL
2 May and 3 May, 1980. Whole set for
both nights.

74. DRURY LANE, LONDON
1980. Whole set broadcast in two parts
on Capital radio. Recording has since
been revealed to be from The Lyceum!

75. LEIDEN, HOLLAND
3 October, 1981.

76. LYON, FRANCE
1 October, 1981.

STEVE HACKETT TAPES

1. CHATEAU NEUF, OSLO
4 October, 1978.
First live gig.

2. MANCHESTER
4 June, 1980.

3. BOTTOM LINE CLUB, NEW YORK
29 September, 1980.

4. READING FESTIVAL – CURE ALL
28 August, 1981.

5. THE HAGUE, HOLLAND
25 September, 1981.

6. LIVERPOOL
3 October, 1981.

TAPES

BIBLIOGRAPHY

1. GENESIS – THE EVOLUTION OF A ROCK BAND Armando Gallo. Sidgwick and Jackson Ltd., London 1978.
ISBN 0283-98440-6 (Paperback).
ISBN 0283-98439-2 (Clothbound).
Out of print.

2. GENESIS LYRICS Illustrated by Kim Poor. Sidgwick and Jackson Ltd., London 1979.
ISBN 0283-98526-7 (Clothbound).
ISBN 0283-98527-5 (Paperback).
Kim Poor is married to Steve Hackett.

3. GENESIS – I KNOW WHAT I LIKE Armando Gallo. D.I.Y. Books Inc., P.O. Box 2055, Hollywood, California 90028, U.S.A., 1980.
Library of Congress Catalogue Number 79-92770. Softback, hardback, plus limited edition of 1,000 leatherbound.
ISBN 0283-987030.

4. GENESIS SONGBOOK (First edition) With interviews by Steve Clark. Wise Publications, London, 1977.
ISBN 0-86001-352-9/AM19241.
Music to 'A Trick Of The Tail' and others.
Out Of Print.

5. GENESIS SECONDS OUT (Reprint of Genesis Songbook)
Wise Publications, London 1978.
ISBN 0 86001 352 9/AM19241.
Selected music from the double live album.

6. GENESIS . . . AND THEN THERE WERE THREE . . . – MUSIC BOOK
Wise Publications, London 1978.
ISBN 0 86001 577 7/AM22658.
All the music from the album.

7. GENESIS – A TRICK OF THE TAIL/WIND AND WUTHERING – MUSIC BOOK Wise Publications, London 1980.
ISBN 0 86001 696 X/AM25438.
All the music to both albums.

8. GENESIS – DUKE – MUSIC BOOK
Wise Publications, London 1980.
ISBN 0 86001 749 4/AM26360.
All the music to the album.

9. ANTHONY PHILLIPS – SIX PIECES FOR GUITAR – MUSIC BOOK
Josef Weinberger Ltd. 1980.

10. PHIL COLLINS – FACE VALUE – MUSIC BOOK Wise Publications, London 1981.
ISBN 0 86001 908 X/AM28879.
All the music to the album.

11. GENESIS – ABACAB – MUSIC BOOK Chappell and Co. Ltd., 1982.
1-2-50764. All the music to the album.

12. GENESIS – THREE SIDES LIVE – MUSIC BOOK
Chappell and Co. Ltd.
Most of the music to the double album, plus colour photos and article on the band.

13. GENESIS – THE ILLUSTRATED DISCOGRAPHY
Geoff Parkyn, Omnibus Press Ltd, London 1983.
OP 42092/ISBN 0.7119.0163.5.
Listing of worldwide Genesis and solo releases.

Genesis

NEW SINGLE

KEEP IT DARK
TAKEN FROM THE ALBUM 'ABACAB'

7" (CB 391) C/W NAMINANU
(PREVIOUSLY UNRELEASED)

12" (CB 391-12) C/W NAMINANU
+ ABACAB
(LONG VERSION)

CHARISMA RECORDS

PROGRAMMES
GENESIS

1. LINDISFARNE/GENESIS – TOUR AUTUMN '72
Genesis notes by Jerry Gilbert. Designed by ROC Advertising Ltd.

2. GENESIS COMPENDIUM – OCTOBER 1973
Included poster, sticker, cardboard cut-out 'Genesis' dice and revolver, plus programme notes by Michael Wale. Designed and produced by Alan Smith.

3. GENESIS – THE LAMB LIES DOWN ON BROADWAY
Includes Peter Gabriel's album sleeve notes. Blue Egg Printing and Design Ltd.

4. GENESIS WORLD TOUR 1977
Notes by Barbara Charone. Designed by ANT/Design Machine.

5. GENESIS EUROPEAN TOUR '77 – PICTURE BOOK
Photography by Robert Ellis. Designed by ANT/Design Machine.

6. GENESIS POSTER/PROGRAMME 1978
Notes by Armando Gallo. Designed by Hipgnosis.

7. KNEBWORTH – A MIDSUMMER NIGHT'S DREAM 24 JUNE 1978
Notes by Hugh Fielder. Photography by Robert Ellis.

8. GENESIS – SUMMERTIME OPEN AIR FESTIVAL 1978
Programme notes in English and German.

9. GENESIS – A FILM OF A ROCK BAND AND THEIR MUSIC 1976
Film brochure. Design by John Elvin. Produced by Prestige Design Ltd.

10. GENESIS – TOUR OF JAPAN 1978
Photos by Armando Gallo. Design by Sujuro Hinatayama. Udo Artists Inc. Presentation 1978.

11. GENESIS IN CONCERT 1980
Photos by Armando Gallo and Phil Kamin. Design by Peter Hill and David Costa for Jubilee Graphics.

12. GENESIS – ABACAB 1981
Designed by David Costa. Published by Broken Arrow Productions. UK copies included Abacab album lyrics.

13. GENESIS 1983
From 'Three Sides Live' tour, by Adrian Hopkins Promotions. Includes text by Andy Mackrill on Genesis tour preparations.

PETER GABRIEL
PROGRAMMES

1. GABRIEL – AUTUMN 1977
Designed by Hipgnosis/Colin Elgie. Marketed by Moonchild Productions.

2. PETER GABRIEL POSTERGRAMME CHRISTMAS 1978
Produced by Brockum Intl. Ltd.

3. PETER GABRIEL – TOUR OF CHINA 1984
'Little Red Book'. Notes by Peter Gabriel, lyrics to third album. Produced by Adrian Hopkins Promotions.

4. PETER GABRIEL – CRYSTAL PALACE 1983

5. PETER GABRIEL – PLAYTIME 1988
From 1983 tour, produced by Adrian Hopkins Promotions. Includes lyrics, photos, discography, etc.

VIDEO FILMS

PROMOTIONAL

GENESIS

1. GENESIS IN CONCERT
BBC 1972.

2. GENESIS ON THE ROAD
BBC Nationwide Documentary 1978.

3. GENESIS – 'FOLLOW YOU FOLLOW ME'
1978.

4. PHIL COLLINS WITH BRAND X
BBC 1979.

5. CELEBRATION – GENESIS
Granada TV 1980.

6. GENESIS – 'TURN IT ON AGAIN'
1980.

7. GENESIS AT THE LYCEUM
BBC Old Grey Whistle Test 1980.

8. GENESIS 'MÍSUNDERSTANDING'
Los Angeles 1980.

9. GENESIS 'ABACAB'
BBC Top Of The Pops 1981.

10. GENESIS 'ABACAB'
Shepperton 1981.

11. KEEP IT DARK
1981.

12. PAPERLATE
BBC Top Of The Pops 1982.

13. MAMA
1983.

14. THAT'S ALL
1983.

15. THAT'S ALL
BBC 'Late Late Breakfast Show' 1983.

16. ILLEGAL ALIEN
Shepperton Studios, 1984.

PETER GABRIEL

1. PETER GABRIEL ON KATE BUSH TV SPECIAL
1980.

2. PETER GABRIEL 'GAMES WITHOUT FRONTIERS'
1980.

3. PETER GABRIEL 'I DON'T REMEMBER'
1980.

4. SHOCK THE MONKEY
1982.

5. I HAVE THE TOUCH
1982.

VIDEO FILMS

PHIL COLLINS

1. JOHN MARTYN IN CONCERT
BBC 1980.

2. PHIL COLLINS 'IN THE AIR TONIGHT'
Tiswas (ITV) 1981.

3. PHIL COLLINS 'IN THE AIR TONIGHT'
BBC Top Of The Pops 1981.

4. PHIL COLLINS 'I MISSED AGAIN'
BBC Top Of The Pops 1981.

5. PHIL COLLINS 'IF LEAVING ME IS EASY'
BBC Top Of The Pops 1981.

6. THRU' THESE WALLS
1982.

7. YOU CAN'T HURRY LOVE
1982.

TONY BANKS

1. THIS IS LOVE
1983.

COMMERCIAL GENESIS

1. THE SHOUT starring Alan Bates, Susannah York, John Hurt (Rank Video). Film soundtrack by Tony Banks and Mike Rutherford.

2. VIDEOSTARS (Thorn EMI Video) 'Top Of The Pops' type compilation, includes Genesis 'No Reply At All', and Phil Collins 'In The Air Tonight'.

3. THREE SIDES LIVE (Thorn EMI Video)
90 mins of live footage and interviews from 1981 tour.

4. NOW THAT'S WHAT I CALL MUSIC VIDEO (Picture Music/Virgin Video)
Includes Genesis 'That's All'.

PHIL COLLINS

1. SECRET POLICEMAN'S OTHER BALL Includes Phil Collins.

2. PRINCES TRUST ROCK GALA
Includes Phil Collins on stage with Pete Townshend, Ian Anderson, Kate Bush, Robert Plant, and solo.

3. PHIL COLLINS VIDEO EP (Picture Music Video)
Includes promo videos of 'In The Air Tonight', 'Thru' These Walls', 'I Missed Again', and 'You Can't Hurry Love'.

4. PHIL COLLINS LIVE AT PERKINS
PALACE (Picture Music Video)
Approx 60 mins of live footage and
interviews, from Perkins Palace,
Pasadena, California.

CONTACT

1. GENESIS INFORMATION
P.O. Box 107, London N6 5RU, England.
Quarterly Genesis Magazine.

2. GENESIS INFORMATION
P.O. Box 253, Princeton Junction 08550,
USA.
Quarterly Genesis Magazine, same as
above and covering North America.

3. FRIENDS OF PETER GABRIEL
P.O. Box 35, Bath BA1 1YJ, Avon,
England.
Includes regular 'Gabbleratchet' news
sheet.

Genesis